# SALUTE TO THE VILLAGE

# SALUTE TO THE VILLAGE

by

## FAY INCHFAWN

*Illustrated by A. E. Bestall*

FOLLY BOOKS

2nd Edition Folly Books 2010

First published by Lutterworth Press 1943

This edition is published by agreement with
The Lutterworth Press

A catalogue record for this book is available from the
British Library

ISBN 978-0-9564405-0-1

Published by Folly Books
Monkton Farleigh
BA15 2QP
www.follybooks.co.uk

Typeset by Vicky

Printed and bound in Great Britain by
J F Print Ltd, Sparkford

## Introduction

### FAY INCHFAWN

Fay Inchfawn was born Elizabeth Rebecca Daniels at Portishead near Bristol on 2 December 1880. Her mother's family appears to have been a distant scion of the wealthy Arundell clothier dynasty of Minchinhampton in Gloucestershire and, certainly, hers seems to have been a secure, middle-class childhood. Although her father's profession is unrecorded it is known that he preached in a minor, non-conformist congregation known as The Brethren, broadly similar in religious outlook to the liberal Baptist movement, which met at a small chapel called Little Bethel in Portishead. Her gentle religious upbringing – all the Christian virtues administered with a light touch – formed and moulded virtually every aspect of her later life. Non-conformity was not always an easy option in late-Victorian England. Confiding to a fellow student, after being sent off to boarding-school at the age of sixteen, that she and her family were members of The Brethren, she was sternly warned that *here, that is a name held in derision*.

From early childhood Elizabeth Daniels suffered from a form of nervous debility that confounded her family's medical advisors but which was, in all probability, a form of multiple encephalitis, or ME. It was her frailty that persuaded the family to move from *Whitegates*, their former home near the centre of Portishead to *Hightower*, a converted farmhouse up in the clear air on the cliffs above the Bristol Channel. Even before her tenth birthday Elizabeth was aware that she wanted to write and it was during the enforced idleness of one of her frequent bouts of childhood illness that she conjured up in her mind her literary *alter-ego*, an imaginary Irish authoress whom she named 'Fay Inchfawn'.

Her first literary ventures consisted of short essays submitted to the Excelsior Club, an exclusively women-only manuscript group in which members made constructive criticism of each other's work. Samples of her work were also submitted to the Scribbling Club, a similar group but open to members of both sexes. There they caught the attention of a fellow member, Atkinson Ward, who was involved with yet another literary society that published a periodical entitled *The Literary Aspirant*. Ward suggested that examples of Elizabeth Daniel's work should be published in *The Literary Aspirant* but she declined the offer. Undeterred by this apparent rebuff Atkinson Ward, while on a cycling holiday in the West Country, sent a message to Elizabeth asking if he could visit. Unable to put him off at short notice she agreed, with some misgiving, to meet him. Initially, she feigned detachment and thus Ward found himself in conversation with Elizabeth's mother and her younger sister Gertrude, who he asked to relay to Elizabeth the message that, in his opinion, 'there is no writer in any of the clubs who can write like Fay Inchfawn'. Despite the inauspicious start, their relationship eventually blossomed and on 26 May 1911 Atkinson and Elizabeth were married at the Little Bethel chapel in Portishead, where special arrangements had been made to allow the solemnization to take place.

Atkinson Ward had began a career in journalism in his home town of Leicester at the age of fourteen but by the time he met Elizabeth Daniels he had moved to Kent where he worked on the *Broadstairs Echo*. After their marriage Elizabeth continued to write occasional articles for various periodicals, but in 1912 her husband suggested they collaborate on a more sophisticated venture – a children's book entitled *Golliwog News*. Although the concept of *Golliwog News*, a story about three children and a toy newspaper (unusual in that it included, folded within its covers, a readable miniature newspaper with articles written for children), was originated by Atkinson Ward, it was almost entirely written by Elizabeth. Once the manuscript was complete Atkinson declared himself too busy with other affairs to spend time marketing it so Elizabeth, now heavily pregnant with her first child, was despatched to London to find a publisher. She first approached Harry Golding at Ward, Lock & Co, probably on the strength of some contributions she had made to the *Windsor Magazine*, but was politely turned down. From there she trudged around to the offices of George Allen & Unwin where, much to her surprise, she was admitted to the office of Allen himself who, after some encouraging remarks, suggested she go instead to S.W. Partridge & Co, for whom her work, Allen told her, might be more suitable. *Golliwog News* was eventually published by Partridge in 1913 under the dual pen-names of Phillip and Fay Inchfawn.

With the increasing financial pressures following the birth of their daughter, Mary, the Ward family decided that Atkinson's small salary from the *Broadstairs Echo* and Elizabeth's unpredictable income from freelance journalism were precariously inadequate, so they discussed the possibility of finding a small business – either a bookshop or stationer's – somewhere in the West Country. Shortly before the outbreak of war in 1914 they discovered a seemingly suitable shop in the centre of the small Wiltshire market town of Bradford-on-Avon. The shop, which was owned by two elderly spinster sisters, the eccentric Misses Merrett, was described by Elizabeth as 'a high gabled building set in surely the most awkward of corners'. The deal was agreed when it was discovered that along with the shop the Merrett sisters were prepared to include their house in Iona Terrace on the Frome Road in Bradford-on-Avon for the very reasonable rent of £14 per year. Elizabeth was distressed to find that the house in Iona Terrace, although no more than fifteen years old, had no bathroom and that the sanitary conveniences were most rudimentary in nature, and situated at the end of the garden.

At the beginning of the Great War Atkinson Ward was declared medically unfit for overseas service (in 1915 he was given the conscription grade C3 – fit only for sedentary service at home camps), and was never enlisted. Throughout the war the shop became increasingly profitable due largely to the increasing trade from early opening to cater for workers, eager for war news, buying newspapers prior to starting the 6 a.m. shift at Spencer Moulton's rubber factory in the town. Ward, although an indifferent journalist, was an astute businessman, and saw the war as a great financial opportunity. During the war he purchased larger premises in the nearby woollen town of Trowbridge and opened a branch of his business there, installing his younger brother Tom in a flat over the shop to manage it. By the end of the war the Wards' financial situation was such that they were able to move, in September 1919, to *The Croft*, a much larger house on the Trowbridge Road in Bradford-on-Avon.

By this time Elizabeth, too, was generating a reasonable income from a regular series of short stories and from weekly poems published in *The Sunday Companion*. In 1920 her first full-length book, a volume of poems entitled *The Verse Book Of A Homely Woman*, was published under her nom de plume of Fay Inchfawn. This slim volume seemed to resonate with the values of the time and sold in huge numbers across the globe, going into twenty-two reprints over a period of twenty-four years. The *Verse Book Of A Homely Woman* was the first of almost forty subsequent books, many of them reflecting her own deep feeling on spiritual themes. She also wrote on commonplace everyday themes and on nature but always with a gentleness and sense of fun that endeared her to her many readers worldwide.

In 1924, when her daughter Mary, known to everyone as 'Bunty', was eleven years old, Elizabeth decided it was time for her to move from Miss Cockram's private school in St Margaret's Street, Bradford-on-Avon. It was hoped that she might attend a girl's school of considerable repute on Lansdown Hill in the nearby city of Bath. Atkinson Ward, however, thought his daughter too frail to undertake the daily eight-mile journey and determined instead that she should attend the local Fitzmaurice Grammar School, a decision that did not go down well with some of the Wards' acquaintances. In one of her autobiographical volumes, *Not The Final Word*, Elizabeth recounts how:

'Some adverse opinions were offered. Bunty's special friend, Margot, had a mother who shuddered at the idea of allowing her daughter to attend the same school as her charwoman's girl. There were others whose ideas were similar but who were courteous enough not to mention them.'

By the mid-1920s Elizabeth's income from her literary work was substantial and in 1927 the family decided to move from Bradford-on-Avon to a large, detached mid-Victorian villa on the boundary between the nearby villages of Freshford and Limpley Stoke. Living at *The Croft* had become vexatious; heavy lorries and buses rumbled past the house at all times of the day and night, local louts noisily congregated every evening around a lamp-post near the front gate, and the daily rounds of social calls were wearying to Elizabeth's delicate constitution. The new house stood in almost four acres of grounds between Crow Hill and Church Lane and was one of three minor mansions (the others being *The Grange* and *Aroona*), all built within a few years of each other in the late 1840s and all, from their elevated positions, commanding spectacular views to the south down the Avon Valley. The architecture is a very diluted and simplified version of the Italianate style used by Goodridge for a number of houses built on Bathwick Hill at much the same time. When the Wards purchased the house it was called *The Laurels* – an apt name, for the garden to the north-east of the house was a vast and forbidding shrubbery of overgrown laurels, while further dense banks of laurel bushes lined the driveways to the north and south of the house. Bunty, however, like her mother, was deeply obsessed by Irish popular culture and was a devotee of W.B. Yeats (at the time still a living, contemporary poet at the age of 62), and at her suggestion the house was renamed *Innisfree*, after Yeats' most enduring poem *The Lake Isle of Innisfree*:

> I will arise and go now, and go to Innisfree,
> And a small cabin build there, of clay and wattles made;
> Nine bean rows will I have there, a hive for honey bee,
> And live alone in a bee-loud glade

The first line of the second verse – 'And I shall have some peace there, for peace comes dropping slow' – perhaps encapsulates the tranquillity Elizabeth hoped to find at *Innisfree*.

*Innisfree*, and Elizabeth's growing involvement in the day-to-day life of the village of Freshford gave inspiration for many of her later books. *Journal of a Tent Dweller* was written while the house was being made ready and is laced in places with rather dark passages as the author is overtaken by her strange illness, exacerbated, in all probability, by the stress of the move. *Living in a Village* and *Salute to the Village* are more upbeat accounts of day-to-day life in Freshford in peace and war, while her children's book *Who Goes to the Wood?* is set almost exclusively in the fields between the Inn at Freshford and Freshford Mill.

A recurrent theme through much of Elizabeth Ward's later work is the Problem of Suitable Domestic Servants. The Servant Problem seems, since the end of the First World War, to have been universal amongst middle-class families throughout Britain and is a subject never far below the surface of much of the popular biography and fiction, particularly comic fiction, of the nineteen-twenties and 'thirties. It is a curious characteristic of domestic servants that they seemed to survive in English fiction long after their counterparts in real life passed into history. Most of the middle-class families and aged spinsters that inhabited spotless cottages in twee rural villages in the novels of Agatha Christie still maintained staffs of house-maids and cooks well into the 1960s. Similarly, servants figure highly in virtually all of Richmal Crompton's *William* stories, even though almost half of the thirty-eight books were written after the outbreak of war in 1939. Although sustained by her dutiful cook/housekeeper, Mrs Nonesuch (or *Nonsuch*, as she appears in some books), Elizabeth seems to have suffered agonies through the want of reliable housemaids. Here, I must admit to a personal interest, for my mother, Dorothy Nesta Doel, was for a while in the 1930s one of the less successful housemaids at *Innisfree*. There seems to have been between Elizabeth and Dorothy a muted hostility, probably fostered by my mother whose temperament was overburdened neither by sympathy nor compassion. It is she, I fear, whom Elizabeth refers to as 'a sour face at Christmas' while my mother, in later years, recounted how she worked for 'a finicky old authoress at *Innisfree* who always pretended she was ill and annoyed everyone by having them constantly carry her on her sick bed to different places in the garden in search of shade'.

For a while, it seems, the Wards were able to do without servants and appeared briefly jubilant at the prospect, for in the first few lines of *Salute to the Village* Elizabeth announces that: 'Bunty and I – in spite of national clouds and prophesies of coming troubles – were having the time of our lives. *We were managing without a maid.*' The elation did not last, however, for by the war's end they were asking the question:

'Would we consider a young maid? Indeed we would. She would be able to wash up, and clean the front door step, and peel potatoes and go to post. Beyond that I had not much hope, for in former days I had suffered from the inefficiencies of the young and immature. They had dropped water and coal and ash all over the house; their breakages were numerous, and chips even more so.'

Eventually a new maid, Esmé, was found – 'Her mother had trained her well, and at fifteen she was an eager learner. From being a helpful buttress to *Innisfree* she became a pillar.' After some six years the domestic stability of *Innisfree* was once again disrupted when Esmé announced that she was engaged to be married. In the changed circumstances of the post-war world, young girls no longer aspired to domestic service, housemaids could not be got and, with increasing age and without domestic help, Elizabeth and her husband found the upkeep of house and grounds increasingly onerous. So *Innisfree* was put on the market.

The early post-war years were a time of austerity; no-one wanted to take on rambling, inconvenient houses like *Innisfree* and those with money to spend were looking for functional, cheap to run and easily maintained houses with all the conveniences of modern living. No buyer could be found and things looked hopeless, until salvation appeared in the form of *Verity*.

Almost twenty years earlier, Elizabeth had run a small class for children in Bradford-on-Avon, including Bunty, who did not attend the conventional Sunday School. There she was helped by a girl, some years older than Bunty, whose name was Vera but whom everyone knew as Verity. As a young woman Verity took the position of friend-companion to an older woman who was an acquaintance of Elizabeth. Over the intervening period Verity and Elizabeth lost contact but, some eighteen years later, just as *Innisfree* was being fruitlessly offered for sale, Elizabeth heard that the old friend had recently died and that Verity was alone and without a position. She was at once invited to *Innisfree* where she performed the roles of secretary to both Elizabeth and Atkinson, and *aide-de-camp* to Bunty as assistant housekeeper. Verity's position was more personal than a mere employee: in her autobiography *Something More To Say* Elizabeth explains that since Verity's arrival at *Innisfree* 'her life and ours have become so interwoven it almost seems as though she has always been with us. The years as they pass have seen us all united in a fellowship of hearts.'

In February 1965 Atkinson Ward, still working at the age of 83, slipped on a frost-damaged kerbstone while walking from his shop in Bradford-on-Avon to the bank, sustaining what appeared initially to be a superficial injury to his head. Recovery was slower and more erratic than anticipated and in September he suffered a slight stroke. On 4 October Elizabeth wrote to a friend from her earliest days in Bradford-on-Avon: 'My husband was suddenly taken ill while getting up, and since then we have lived through many days when Hope and Dread have seemed to be striving for mastery.' Atkinson Ward died the following evening.

Elizabeth, Bunty and the indispensable Verity stayed on at *Innisfree* until the early 1970s. A large area of the garden known as the Paddock was sold for development and two detached bungalows built there. In 1974, with the upkeep of *Innisfree* sapping the energies and finances of the three now aging women, Elizabeth had a new house, named *Glenthorne* in memory of a much-loved bible teacher from her childhood days, built in the grounds just to the north of (and rather overshadowed by) the old house, which passed into the hands of new owners. Elizabeth died on 16 April 1978 at the age of 98 and her daughter Bunty just five years later in 1983. Both are buried alongside Atkinson in the graveyard of St Mary's, Limpley Stoke. Verity was left to enjoy the benefit of *Glenthorne* for the duration of her life. Visitors to the house shortly before Verity died remember rooms still overflowing with manuscripts and notes for Elizabeth's books.

## SALUTE TO THE VILLAGE

Writing about *Salute To The Village* in her autobiographical memoir *Those Remembered Days*, Elizabeth reminds us that:

> 'A great deal has been packed into this book, including the arrival of evacuees. *Salute* was written while things mentioned were actually happening, and this, I think, is why it found favour, so many others were experiencing similar distresses.'

Many original manuscripts, all the printer's plates and the publisher's entire stock of over twenty-five of Elizabeth's books were lost when Lutterworth's warehouse and offices were destroyed in the Blitz. It was arranged that *Salute To The Village* should be printed in America, but the manuscript was intercepted en-route by the official censor who requested that many passages should be expunged before publication be allowed. The limestone hills around Freshford and Limpley Stoke are riddled with abandoned stone quarries, seemingly endless labyrinths of tunnels extending over many acres one hundred feet below the ground. One of these quarries, just a few hundred yards from *Innisfree*, had been requisitioned by the Ministry of Supply and was filled with one hundred thousand tons of TNT destined for bomb-filling factories in South Wales. Part of another larger quarry at Westwood, a mile or so up the Avon valley towards Bradford-on-Avon, had been converted into an underground factory manufacturing war materiel while another part was used to store priceless artefacts evacuated from the great museums and art galleries of London. Mention of all these sites was struck out of the manuscript of *Salute To The Village*, although references to the pillboxes, and to a searchlight site in the village, were passed for publication.

Infuriatingly, in all of her biographical and what may be loosely termed 'topographical' books, including *Salute To The Village*, Fay Inchfawn seems randomly to employ pseudonyms for many proper nouns. In *Salute To The Village*, nowhere is the name 'Freshford' used, although all the clues are obvious enough. Within the village the names of some people, houses and geographical features are changed while others, equally recognisable, are not. Some changes are blatant and are immediately decodable, others are more subtle. Thus, the *City of the West* is obviously Bristol and the *Roman City* is Bath. Less obviously, *Broadwater* is Bradford-on-Avon, *Bridgeford* is Trowbridge and *Woodwick* is the village of Westwood. Of the houses in the village, a wonderful Arts and Crafts property, standing high on a precipitous rocky outcrop overlooking Sharpstone, known in reality as *The Hermitage*, is, in the book, transformed into *The Chantry*. Fay Inchfawn's *Mavoureen* is actually *Aroona*, bought in 1864 by Frederick Hayward, an English entrepreneur returned from Australia where he had made his fortune during the boom in sheep farming there. The house was named in memory of Aroona Station, the Hayward's estate in Australia. The pseudonym *Mavoureen* is derived from an Irish Gaelic term meaning 'my beloved' and its use once again reflects the author's infatuation with Irish culture and folklore. *The Hydro* refers to the Limpley Stoke Hotel, once a hydropathic institution trading on its close proximity to Bath but long descended into a run-of-the-mill commercial hotel. During the Second World War the London headquarters of the Abbey National Building Society (Fay Inchfawn's *Belfry Road Building Society*) was evacuated there.

The *Little Grey Church* is the church of St Mary, Limpley Stoke. Although non-conformist by conviction, Elizabeth Ward adopted her husband's religious beliefs after their marriage and worshipped – and was buried – beside him at St Mary's. Of the other locations mentioned in the book, Friary Woods is correctly named and lies to the south-west of the village, sandwiched between the river Frome and the A36 trunk road. The remote hamlet of Friary, a handful of houses widely dispersed about a common, occupies a clearing in the woods. *Weir Island* is an artificial island in the river Frome formed behind Freshford mill by the alignment of the mill race and leat. During the early part of the twentieth century it was a popular picnic location, accessed by a narrow footbridge. During the Second World War the former woollen mill was adapted for use in the rubber industry. Before the days of environmental control much toxic waste from the factory was poured into the river at this point and the island became somewhat insalubrious. It is now inaccessible and only the brick abutments of the bridge survive.

The section of *Salute To The Village* which mentions the evacuees who appeared in the village, having nightly trekked from the City of Bath, refers to the shameful bombing of the city on the nights of 25 and 26 April, 1942 as part of the Luftwaffe's 'Baedeker' campaign, targeted against British cultural centres in reprisal for British air raids against Lübeck. Over the two nights of the raid more than four hundred people were killed and two thousand buildings in the historic Georgian city either destroyed or severely damaged.

The final historical reference that may require explanation concerns the 'block houses, cleverly camouflaged to look like old sheds, hayricks or small cottages'. These were pillboxes built along the defence lines established in haste in the spring of 1940 to protect London, Bristol and the industrial Midlands from an invading German army. Three important elements of these defence lines converged at Freshford, one running from the south coast and up the valley of the river Frome, another running east from Freshford towards Reading along the line of the Kennet and Avon Canal, with a third curving away to the north-west to form an eastern defensive arc around the port of Bristol. The 'mighty ditch' that Fay Inchfawn witnessed under construction was a section of deep anti-tank ditch that was supposed to stretch the breadth of southern England though very little was actually completed before the scheme was abandoned. Little of this massive wartime undertaking still survives except for a small section, miraculously preserved, in Hogg Wood at Pipehouse, just north of Freshford.

*Nick McCamley*
*Monkton Farleigh, October 2009*

# CONTENTS

| Chapter | | Page |
|---|---|---|
| I | THE LAST DAYS OF PEACE | 1 |
| | *O Loved And Lovely England!* | 10 |
| | *Britannia At Iford* | 11 |
| II | THE FIRST DAYS OF WAR | 13 |
| | *Oh, Can It Be In Times Like These!* | 21 |
| | *Let Us Be The People Of The Plough!* | 22 |
| III | THE VILLAGE ENTERTAINS STRANGERS | 23 |
| | *England Calling To Her Children* | 35 |
| | *The Answer Of England's Children* | 36 |
| IV | THE TURN OF THE YEAR | 37 |
| | *The Days Ahead* | 48 |
| | *If I Could Choose* | 48 |
| V | THE LONG LULL | 49 |
| | *Easter Eve* | 56 |
| | *Rogationtide* | 57 |
| VI | THE MONTH OF MAY | 59 |
| | *The Man Of The Hour* | 70 |
| | *These Are Great Days* | 71 |
| VII | UNDER THE SHADOW OF INVASION | 73 |
| | *England, I Have Never Told You* | 82 |
| | *When England Falls* | 83 |
| VIII | THE SOUND OF THE SIREN | 85 |
| | *That Dreaded Hour* | 94 |
| | *To The Axis* | 95 |
| IX | DAYS OF DANGER | 97 |
| | *City Of The West* | 105 |
| | *Women Of Britain* | 106 |

X THE DOWNS AND THE UPS . . . . 109
*Peace May Come To Earth Again!* . . . . 118
*England Keeps Christmas* . . . . . 119

XI THE VILLAGE IS STIRRED . . . . 121
*You – Who Will Carry Old England On* . . . 126
*Singapore* . . . . . . . 127

XII FIRE WATCHERS . . . . . . 129
*Night Duty* . . . . . . . 135

XIII RAIDS ON THE ROMAN CITY . . . . 137
*Stones Of Britain* . . . . . . 145

XIV THE CHANGES WHICH ARE SURE TO COME . . 147
*There Is So Much To Love In England* . . . 156

XV A DREADED VISITATION . . . . . 157
*A Litany For Cattle Men* . . . . . 166
*England's Son* . . . . . . . 167

XVI THIS IS MY VILLAGE . . . . . 169

*Chapter One*

## THE LAST DAYS OF PEACE

IT WAS THAT SEASON OF THE YEAR WHEN YOUNG MARTINS are leaning out of nests shouting for flies; when white lilies and limes are in bloom, raspberries crying out to picked and everything is over-growing itself.

It was also at this season that Bunty and I – in spite of national clouds and prophecies of coming troubles – were having the time of our lives. *We were managing without a maid.*

This statement regarding our jubilant feelings is not quite so boastful as it sounds. We are, neither of us, really fond of any sort of work. We can sit quite happily in deck chairs on a sunny bank, without desiring to spring-clean the house or to pull up all the weeds in the garden.

But somewhere, deeply within us, I think we must each of us possess a streak of pure housewifeliness. If not, why should we so thoroughly enjoy having kitchen, china pantry and larder entirely to ourselves and under our own eyes?

We had had this pleasure for quite a protracted season, because our daily helper, Mrs. Nonesuch, was (by doctor's orders) taking a long rest. She left us with great reluctance, and with many solemn injunctions not to over-tire ourselves. As soon as she came back she would put everything right which had gone wrong.

We knew this to be no figure of speech. When Mrs. Nonesuch goes round the house, dust disappears from stairs, brass becomes shiny, curtains hang perfectly straight. Each room assumes a cared-for, up-together spruce appearance, and the tiles at the back door dry out clean and spotless with no smudges.

We knew we could not trust ourselves to keep the house as Mrs. Nonesuch would like to find it, and we looked round for some capable woman who would give us two hours or so each morning.

We looked in vain, and we were wondering what we could devise, when Michael came to the rescue. Our Irish Michael, at certain seasons of the year, finds the garden too much for him, and he has to get Maxwell in. Maxwell was at this very time helping Michael with the clipping, and Maxwell had once been a butler!

Michael said that he would, if we wished it, spare Maxwell to come in every morning, to go over the rooms and do any washing-up. Maxwell proved to be a most efficient houseman, quiet, quick and thorough.

Bunty went to her office in the mornings, and had only to get our meals, and help to preserve the fruit, which every day seemed to hurry a little ahead of us. In the cool of the day we picked raspberries and red currants, and made them into jams and jellies.

The scent of the limes came in at every window. Sometimes we had warm rainy nights and, suddenly, that deliciously summery sweetness came to me in my half-dreaming state. Day and night the bees were clinging about the limes. The most contented and joyous of sounds is surely the humming of innumerable winged creatures as they sip honey from lime-blossoms.

Leaning out of the window very early to draw in more of that indescribable fragrance, I saw on the lawn a queer, humped-up looking bird. At breakfast time it was still in the same place and posture. Armed with field glasses John went out to investigate. He returned to tell me the bird was a young cuckoo, and two hedge-sparrows were feeding it.

A young *cuckoo*! As soon as John said the words my thoughts began to piece together a small fragment of one of the biographies which are always being written in our garden. Inscribed on blades of grass, on branches of trees, and on the brown earth itself, if only we knew the language well enough to read it!

I remembered that one morning in May I had been walking round the garden when I heard quite a loud bang not very far away. Bursts of motor-bicycle exhausts, and the clamp of railway trucks reach even into our solitude, and use has dulled our ears so that we take little notice of them.

It was lilac and laburnum time, and I was walking slowly when I saw close to the house, and under the drawing-room window, a large greyish bird sitting. It allowed me to approach near enough to see that it was not a pigeon, as I had first thought, but a rarer and slimmer bird. I saw, too, that it was injured – alas, the bang I had heard made it almost certain that these grey and beautiful wings had flown against the window glass.

The bird showed no fear. The golden eyes had no terror in them. Not a feather fluttered as I carried the warm thing into the house. I put it very gently into a soft-lined basket, and left it in a cool dark place out of the reach of cats. This was not the first time birds had struck our windows, and some of them had recovered. But within a few seconds those golden eyes had closed, the beautiful head drooped, and my bird was dead.

It was a cuckoo. The Bird Book plainly declared it. From that curved beak and soft-feathered throat had come "the wandering voice", which in springtime we hear from before dawn till after dusk, calling up and down our valley.

The picture in the Bird Book did nothing approaching justice to the living bird. The plain gray of its outer dress was interlaced with delicate patterns like exquisite tracery. Hitherto, I had thought of the cuckoo as rather an intriguer, one who shifted responsibilities, but if habiliments are any index to character, then the cuckoo must take its place among the gentlefolk.

Watching the baby cuckoo, I wondered: was *my* cuckoo by any chance its parent? And had she just dropped her egg into the hedge-sparrow's nest when she met with the misadventure which caused her death? No one could say. The youngster flourished and finally flew over our high yew hedge into the fields – *en route*, we suppose, for its journey over the sea to lands unknown.

The plums began to ripen and Bunty began to be busy with Red Cross and A.R.P. work. The Village was becoming casualty-minded, and after much lecturing and bandaging, those in authority decided to organize a "black-out".

I would have liked to help with this, but the only assistance that seemed possible was to allow myself to be bandaged at odd times by Bunty and her Red Cross comrades. I think, perhaps, every part of my anatomy has been subjected to the most careful binding up. I have been "put to bed", and had the bed made while in it, by two earnest young persons who supported me with tenderness when slipping the undersheet in, but left me quite callously to get up without assistance, while they practised the art of resuscitation upon each other.

These diligent students were pleased about the "black-out", and the Village was interested but inclined to jeer at the whole proceeding as a harmless, but rather foolish waste of time.

The great night arrived, and at ten minutes to twelve Bunty, in her Red Cross uniform, set off for the casualty station which had once been the stable of the Manor House. This room, which was not large, was lit by three oil lamps and warmed by two oil stoves. Windows were all shut and done up with black paper. About a dozen people were in the room and casualties were very soon being brought in.

Miss Fursden was the first. She was carried in by Maxwell and Michael and, after the label tied to her waist-band had been consulted, was found to be suffering from compound fracture of the ribs.

Mr. Jinks had severe head wounds. Under his cap, to simulate blood-matted hair, protruded a bunch of red shavings from a chocolate box.

Mrs. Jinks – tenderly supported by a female friend – had arterial haemorrhage. Her wrist – carefully lipsticked to look like blood – had a most realistic appearance.

Pad and flexion was, of course, the correct treatment, and this was applied so earnestly that – what with the lamps, the stoves, the shut windows, and the increasing number of injured persons arriving – Mrs. Jinks complained of "feeling faint".

This – the only genuine casualty – had not been anticipated, and the solitary remedy at hand was a bottle of water labelled "Sal Volatile". Mrs. Jinks' bed, however, was carried into the stable yard where the cool air soon revived her.

But the Village next day was contemptuous of the whole affair. The story of the "dead" faint and the bottle of water gathered to itself certain lurid and quite untrue details, which are still cited whenever A.R.P. comes into prominence.

Bunty peeped into my bedroom at about 2 a.m. to let me know she was back. The practice had proved most successful and she had for the first time been addressed as "Nurse".

Staring at her with sleepy eyes and dulled brain, I thought she looked the part. The half-opened door made the curtains blow away from the window. Stars were shining above our quiet valley. How remote war seemed – how entirely unlikely. I grunted something cheerful and – I hope – sympathetic; then the door closed softly and I was asleep again.

The hot weather continued. Bunty had a short holiday, and we went blackberrying.

It was very pleasant to set off in the morning instead of waiting till afternoon. There is a spirit of expectancy and coming adventure in the morning which, later in the day, has toned itself down. "In the morning it flourisheth and groweth up" is a tuneful phrase which may be applied to almost every worth-while undertaking. Some persons seem to get their best thoughts at night, but I have always had mine in the morning. To me that is the time when energy seems boundless, time endless, and all the resources of the universe on their way to meet me.

We started off hopefully carrying large baskets. Though it was early for blackberries, we knew a sunny slope where the very first of them might be found. On her shoulders Bunty had slung her knapsack. In it was a flask containing tea, a bottle of milk, paper packets of sugar and salt, and a parcel of thickly-buttered slices of brown bread. In my basket I had two hard-boiled eggs; two large tomatoes and two hefty slices of home-made sultana cake.

At the corner, just as we were passing the old mill, we met with Mr. Piggott. It is a curious thing, but whenever we go out "stravaging" we nearly always *do* meet with Mr. Piggott – in fact, we are disappointed, and we remark upon it, when we don't.

Mr. Piggott has a countenance like a full and joyful harvest moon. He seems to like meeting us as much as we like meeting him. We stopped to chat with him. He had seen a badger the night before, coming down the wood-path in the moonlight just like you or me.

Asked about the chances of finding blackberries, Mr. Piggott thought them favourable. "If nobody else hasn't had them, and I haven't see'd anyone – what's your Pa think about Hitler, Miss?"

We had not time just then to inform him of all John's thoughts upon that fruitful subject, and after mutual salutations we went on our way.

In the wood there was the old woody smell, scent of innumerable small herbs – wood ruff, cow-parsley and ground ivy; wood vetches and honeysuckles were twined about the trees.

The lightness and promise of Spring had changed into the fulfilment of Summer. Every leaf was out. Light came fitfully through the thick branches. Most of the birds were silent. The Spirit of Beauty walked here – less ecstatically, but more serenely than in the days of April.

We found our sunny slope, and we found blackberries. Large, juicy, first-ripe fruit showing black and beautiful in the midst of clusters only reddening.

We went home feeling particularly jubilant, with full baskets, and we were in the kitchen still jellying when John returned.

Our story of twelve pounds of blackberries in two hours failed to impress him.

He sat for a long time reading his newspaper. He ate salad, cold meat and cheese, with an absent-minded air. Even stewed blackberries, cream and custard might have been dust and ashes in his mouth for all the interest he took in them.

Bunty gave Tigger the Cat his supper. It was liver – which he loved – and he ate it with loud gulps and sucks of appreciation. Bunty said she liked to hear him, and added that it was not much fun slaving for men who did not even purr when things were extra nice.

John laughed at that. But he was "concerned" all the same. The gravity – the intense gravity of the way world affairs were trending had for years weighed upon his spirit. He had frequently said that the day was coming when the British people would be called upon to fight for their existence.

Often I had told him that he was taking too sombre a view,

and when I mentioned the League of Nations he always replied that you couldn't build a new world with the old material. Every child born into the world was a renewal of the old material, and while man existed strife would go on.

So he said!

That night, after Bunty was in bed, we sat talking for a long time. He told me he thought we were approaching one of the climacterics in our history. The unrest of nations was like a pot, boiling within itself all the time, now and then it boiled over, with results that were catastrophic.

"You see," he said – he looked so earnest I wished I could understand better what he knew so well – "you see, it is the balance of power that is shifting. It is always on the move – it lies sometimes with this nation – sometimes with that. Germany is striving for it. Britain has held it.

"But I very much fear that Britain has not got it now. In past years the British Lion had only to shake his shaggy old head, and would-be aggressors drew back. When small nations called for help, we were able to give it. And now – what can we do for Poland if she is attacked? What did we do for the Czechs? We have handed out our promises of assistance, and at the same time denied ourselves the means whereby we can carry out our commitments. In the old days we should have sent a couple of cruisers and a gunboat or two, and the trouble would have stopped. But it will take more than that to stop it to-day."

He said a good deal beside. Said it with earnestness and fervour, and I could not help a feeling of dread and foreboding. It stole over me like a black cloud, shutting out for a moment the little sweet treasured things of life, darkening the immediate future, and making one wonder just how, and just when, the fearsome things were going to happen.

The best thing to do at the moment seemed to be to go to bed. And the next day being very fine Bunty and I journeyed to a certain City in the West, and spent the day with my mother.

Old cities are the truest records of our past; they are history written in stone. We went up the narrow street where William and Dorothy Wordsworth stayed. We went over the river bridge and up the steep incline to the Cathedral. Deep trenches had been dug in the smooth velvet of the College Green. Sandbags were piled before the house of learning called after the Merchant Venturers.

We went on up noble Park Street to the road where White Ladies used to walk, and on until we reached the place where highwaymen waited on Black Boy Hill.

That grand city of the West with her tall ships, her stately churches and square towers was awaiting her future with equanimity. When Spain threatened us with her Armada, the bells from those church towers rang throughout the night their solemn warning of invasion. Would those city bells soon have cause to ring once more a challenge to her citizens to be ready for whatever might come?

My mother's house seemed very quiet and peaceful. She inquired anxiously what John thought of the situation but, except for that inquiry, things appeared to be much as usual. We sat and knitted, talking of family affairs, of old days and of weddings-to-be, until it was time to go home again.

The City by evening light, and at sunsetting, seemed transfigured and ennobled. The tower of her famous explorer shone like a diamond. The river was at high tide, and down the shimmery tideway went the majestic ships moving slowly, stately towards the open sea. Even the railway station was beautiful, that hurrying, screaming, bustling place with its memories – for multitudes – of joyous goings-away.

We reached home in time to get the supper on the table before John arrived. I was very glad to think Maxwell would wash the dishes for us next morning, and I remembered that it would be nice to have Mrs. Nonesuch again.

Very soon Bunty would resume her office work, and I practically decided to take her advice and give myself up to getting a restful week. I would be lazy and let her pick the plums, and look up the laundry, and write the order, while I sat in the sun and let the city-tiredness soak out of me.

Only another fortnight and Mrs. Nonesuch would come back to us energetic and as jolly as ever, and I should be free to write the book which was to be better than any I have written yet.

Then, as often before, I spent a few minutes dreaming over the fabric of this volume. Sometimes it takes the form of a story – sometimes it is partly in verse. In any case this book is to be a rest-encouraging, and not an embarrassing book. It must contain the sort of reading one could safely indulge in during wakeful nights, and never become excited nor frightened thereby.

Of course, there must be a love interest in it, for what is any book worth which makes no mention of this, the most thrilling of earthly experiences? John Milton, when writing of his own aims in putting pen to paper, said he wished "to justify the ways of God to men". In my own humble sphere I have always wanted to do that. In this book which has never been written, I told myself hopefully "perhaps I shall".

Before I went to sleep that night I decided to begin it without any more delayings, but the next few days brought strange and stressful happenings.

Germany made a pact with Russia.

Parliament was recalled.

The King returned to London from Balmoral, and John was busy each night up till a late hour swathing every light in the house in folds of black tissue paper.

All the world was waiting for Hitler. Then Germany attacked Poland, and Mrs. Wills, one of the billeting officers in our village, was discovered standing at our front door.

Mrs. Wills said there was to be an immediate evacuation of mothers and children from London.

Mrs. Wills said she was sending us two mothers and two children.

Mrs. Wills said we could expect them to arrive at tea time on Sunday afternoon.

# O LOVED AND LOVELY ENGLAND!

Where uplands and green valleys smile
The little fields stretch mile on mile,
Lilac with lady-smock, and golded
With dust of buttercups enfolded.
The hawthorn decks her boughs with white
And blackcap whistles for delight.

O loved and lovely England! Now,
How more than ever dear art thou
When a mailed fist and ruthless hand
Is threatening thee – our Motherland!

# BRITANNIA AT IFORD

Rumbling roystering river Frome,
Running through England's greenest room,
Only elect souls catch the swing
Of the mad glad nautical song you sing!

River! Why does Britannia stand
On your gray bridgehead far inland –
Hand on the helm, and her stern face set,
Bent on guardianing England yet –
Listening ever to catch the swing
Of the mad glad nautical song you sing?

Not to the dipper, nor to the wren –
Britannia beckons to England's men!
Follow me far and follow me wide –
I am the wind and I am the tide;
I am the seed and I am the corn;
I am the old and the yet unborn;
I am the English hills and plains,
The English fields and the English lanes,
The English ships and the English sea!
Now, and for all eternity,
I am the whole, and never a part,
Of England's resolute oaken heart.

Rumbling roystering river Frome
Running through England's greenest room,
Only elect souls catch the swing
Of the mad glad nautical song you sing!

## Chapter 2

### THE FIRST DAYS OF WAR

WHEN MRS. WILLS HAD TAKEN HER DEPARTURE BUNTY and I looked at each other.

Two mothers and two children coming to live here in our house! And coming the day after to-morrow!

Feeling as though our eyes were starting out of our heads, our hair standing bolt upright, and our hearts in our boots, we went into the kitchen to begin our preparations.

This house is the best house I know for playing hide-and-seek. The front staircase is close to the front door. On the top of the stairs is the semi-circle of the landing leading round to the back stairs, at the foot of which is the back door. You can run all round in less than a minute, passing all the bedroom doors on the way.

We decided to give the two mothers the large airy bedroom which is nearest to the back stairs, and also a good-sized sitting-room on the ground floor, and to make our china pantry into a kitchenette for their exclusive use.

I will admit that the prospect of parting with the pantry gave me a pang. It is small but compact, with ample shelf space, and nicely divisioned drawers for table-linen, tea-cloths and dust sheets. The cupboards are very handy for sheltering hot-water bottles; the pantry also possesses a porcelain sink. I could scarcely bear to contemplate giving up all these conveniences, yet this seemed to us a lesser evil than having to share our own kitchen with two entirely unknown quantities.

The first thing we did was to assemble and classify the glass and china. We put it into three groups.

Group 1. To be packed up and put away in lumber room.

Group 2. To be found accommodation in the kitchen for our own use.

Group 3. Utensils including saucepans and cutlery for use of evacuees.

We were in the midst of this most colossal muddle when through the pantry window we heard quick hurrying footsteps which could only belong to one person – Mrs. Nonesuch!

For just one joyous moment I thought she had come bent upon life-saving! Alas! the repercussions of a world turned topsy-turvy were finding expression in each of our little lives. Mrs. Nonesuch had come back to tell us that she *couldn't* come back!

She was that very day expecting a mother and two children to be billeted on her, and, of course, she couldn't leave her house to be overrun by folks like that!

We felt very sorry for Mrs. Nonesuch. Her home is, I should think, the neatest, cleanest, most daintily arranged home in our Village. When Bunty and I had been for tea with her, and had seen the whole of her domain, we entreated her to take us as lodgers. Her spare bedroom looks out upon a green hillside, and the wind which comes over that hill smelt to us like wind from the sea.

Mrs. Nonesuch had every single thing in her kitchen in a state of shining cleanliness, and her two sitting-rooms, one at the front and the other at the back of the house, were each of them equally pleasant and beautifully ordered.

We knew it would be torture for her to have to give house-room to strangers, and though we tried to comfort her by saying that perhaps things would not be so bad as we feared, Mrs. Nonesuch could not see any bright spot in the situation. She hurried away at a run to pack up some of her treasures and to make up beds for the invaders.

So that was that!

We still had much to do. Maxwell came in and cleaned the bedroom – he also helped us in removing commodities from the sitting-room. He carried boxes and biscuit tins to their new residences. He helped to clear the larder shelves of empty jars and deposited them in the cellar.

We worked like slaves. Bunty telephoned to the Gas Company. They agreed to send a small cooker and a man to fix it that very afternoon.

We were having a hurried tea, sitting up to the kitchen table, when Bunty paused with plum jam on its way to her mouth:

"What about our jam? Mrs. Wills said we had better keep our private things locked up."

So she had! Our jam – pounds of it – was in the larder and there was no key for the larder door. With the best wish in the world to be trustful of everybody, we both – but Bunty especially – felt that something would have to be done.

Our jam, made with punctilious attention to every detail of boiling, skimming and testing, till one reached the pleasant stage of pouring into carefully counted pots, tying down and labelling! Jam over which so much toil had been expended was entirely different from boughten jam, and infinitely more precious. To leave it unprotected within easy reach of persons who might – but who, also, might *not* – be quite honest, was a course of action entirely unthinkable.

On being consulted about this momentous matter, John thought he had better fetch Mr. Bagshaw. When Mr. Bagshaw came, he said he would have to remove the lock and take it away to make a key. He shook his head over the evacuees, and told us his wife was expecting three. He thought we had better have a key for the kitchen door also.

"You don't want *them* at your grocery cupboard, Madam," said Mr. Bagshaw, grinding and wrenching away with a screwdriver.

I remembered that the door opening into the hall had no key; nor had the door which shut off the back stairs from the front. Mr. Bagshaw accompanied by John went upstairs and the grinding and wrenching began all over again.

Downstairs Michael was busy beating carpets and putting up a roller for a roller towel. His landlady had promised to take four.

Mr. Flower, summoned by phone during the morning, arrived at this inopportune moment to put shelves in the kitchen to give us space for our own china. He was as helpful as ever, and he thought of several contrivances for making the kitchen more convenient, but we fancied he seemed depressed, or not quite so light-hearted as usual. But Mr. Flower was one of the billeting officers and he had much to bear. His hammering and Mr. Bagshaw's wrenching drowned other sounds and we had to shout to make each other hear.

At last all had been done that could be done towards preparation, except that the Gas Company had not sent the cooker. Everything else had gone according to plan.

I think I shall always remember that queer Saturday. England was facing something unknown, something disastrous. Planes roaring overhead had a sinister sound, trains seemed to rumble ominously. I was sitting making black curtains for the bathroom, and strung up to the highest pitch. All the rooms were looking sombre and Machiavellian with black paper swathed round lights, and brown paper pasted at the tops and sides of windows. I was tacking the last hem when Bunty, who had been to the Village, came home with news. She had seen the Ellisons. They had motored all night from London, and were staying at a cottage just below. Mrs. Ellison was coming up to see me.

She came, and our pleasure in seeing her was very great. Mrs. Ellison had for years been our nearest neighbour, and we had seen the upbringing of her two boys, Ian and Melville, and of her little daughter Jane. Two years had passed since Mrs. Ellison moved to London, and now in this stressful hour she had decided to come back with her children and await the arrival of that suddenly crushing onslaught by the enemy, which was expected at any moment.

On Sunday morning our Prime Minister, that great gentleman Mr. Chamberlain, announced that Britain was at war with Germany. It was a solemn hour. What the decision involved we could not in any sense foresee. No one could say we had rushed into war. Every possible means had been taken to avert it.

Less than a year had passed since Hitler had invited Mr. Chamberlain to confer at Munich with Monsieur Daladier and Signor Mussolini. The Führerhaus flew all four flags and each National Anthem was played as the respective ministers arrived. It was a marvellous piece of window-dressing on the part of

Germany.

An Agreement was signed by the representatives of the four powers; our Prime Minister returned and was welcomed with acclamation. He showed the cheering crowd a piece of paper signed by Herr Hitler and himself, which expressed a desire for friendliness between our two countries and a wish that we might never go to war with each other any more! There were some persons who now spoke bitterly against the honourable man who had seemed to be cajoled and hoodwinked. Yet he gained for us nearly a year in which to rectify some of our mistakes of unpreparedness. Mr. Chamberlain knew – much better than the ordinary individual could know – how averse the British Public had been, and still is, to making any personal and protracted effort. John had often told me that only dynamite could persuade the great masses of the people that the danger was real and war imminent.

I knew then, and I know now, that I ought to be the very last person to sit in judgment on them. For, indeed, in my own inner life, I had been too much given to complacency; too anxious to protect my small citadel of peace from disturbing thoughts.

"May God bless you all and defend the right."

With these words Mr. Chamberlain ended his announcement. Bunty and I jumped to our feet for the National Anthem.

John turned off the wireless with a snap and told me I had better lie down and rest. But, like thousands of other British women, I was being carried on the tide of great events, and this for the time being kept me from feeling weariness of any kind. I felt able to keep on turning out cupboards and putting things tidy for ever.

I told John we should all have to do our own work now - and *I* was not going to play the part of an invalid and get favours out of everybody! Feeling very valiant and very confident I quoted with, I am afraid, some arrogance:

> *Must I be carried to the skies*
> *On flowery beds of ease,*
> *While others die to win the prize*
> *And wade through bloody seas?*

Just here Bunty reminded me that we still had to dish the lunch, wash it up and make a pudding for supper, and that the Ellisons were expected for tea. She said that if I would cut the bread and butter she would see to everything else – then we should both be ready to welcome the evacuees whenever they might arrive, which she strongly suspected would be *soon*.

Mrs. Ellison and Jane came at four o'clock. They brought news that the mothers had arrived at the Village Hall! They had been given tea, and three of them, with their children, had been deposited with our mutual friend Mrs. Frobisher at *Mavoureen*.

My heart began doing gymnastics. The house called *Mavoureen* was just up the road. *Our* mothers must arrive within the next few minutes. I sat at the tea-table – to the outward eye, calmly, and on a chair – but my spirit perched upon tenterhooks, wobbled between exhilaration and despair.

A movement outside sent John to the back door. It was only the milk, and after taking an extra quart for the evacuees, he returned to the tea-table.

A resounding rat-tat on the front door made us all rise. Mrs. Ellison said: "Here they are – we will just slip away – we shall be seeing you —— "

But Bunty had opened the door to Ian and Melville Ellison. They came in exuberantly; they had helped to drive the mothers to their destinations.

"But where are Mrs. Inchfawn's?" asked Jane, whose interest and excitement was as great as our own.

The boys could not tell us. They had helped to carry bundles and newspaper parcels, but they drew the line at babies.

"Their luggage," said Mickey, "smelt rather queer – like fish, you know. Have you heard what the Poles are doing today?"

When we all said "No", Melville, his face full of mischief, told us: "They are holding up the telegraph wires."

After the Ellisons had departed, we had several more false alarms, but presently the autumnal evening closed in, dark came down – and no one had arrived.

Still on-the-listen, we had supper; at ten o'clock John locked the doors and we went to bed. That long queer Sunday was over.

I did not feel quite so jubilant now. Of course, the evacuees would come on Monday when John and Bunty were at business, and I should be in the house alone. I did not like the prospect at all. My noble, altruistic, and patriotic feelings, like snow upon the desert's dusty face, had melted quite away.

On Monday morning, just after breakfast, the gas cooker arrived. The men who brought it knew nothing, and could promise nothing, with regard to its being fixed. They dumped it, with its spare parts, just inside the back door, where everyone could fall over it, and went away again.

Maxwell carried the cooker into the pantry, and told me that the evacuees were an awful lot. The heart of the Village was moved as the trees of the wood are moved with the wind. The things Maxwell had heard were, evidently, not suitable for me to know, for when he mentioned "them women" Maxwell lifted his eyebrows and gazed wildly at the ceiling.

All the morning I was busy with the many tidying-up jobs which Monday always brings. As I worked I was thinking over again the situation which had at last begun to touch my own personal life.

Silence and solitude – the two things which have been most precious, and most helpful – must now, I knew very well, be mine no longer. Frankly, *I did not like it.* Soon there would be strange feet upon the stairs, and unaccustomed noises about the house. Children playing and calling and, probably, screaming. Two strange women would be working round and crossing my path, however much I might try to keep out of their way.

To those of us who find the Eternal things real and precious, it is natural that thoughts, when we are alone, should many of them be prayers. Thinking of these two women, I realized that I was more afraid of myself than of them; afraid of my own unwillingness to give away indefinitely my own privacy; afraid of my own selfishness in desiring inordinately to have my life left to me for my own purposes.

John had said the women would probably be an asset rather than a liability. He said he could see them helping me in the house, getting supper ready for us, and doing odd jobs in the kitchen. When he talked like this I began to see myself knitting garments for the children, arranging little treats for them, and looking after them while their mothers had a rest.

Quite sincerely, and truly, I wanted to help my country – yet, as I went round the house and peeped into the nice clean bedroom and the sunny, comfortable sitting-room prepared for our guests, I found myself praying that they might be refined, grateful and agreeable (but not presuming) people. In short, it was the old wish in a slightly different dress. I would like to feel I was being useful – if that usefulness did not put *me* out too much.

Dusting the drawing-room, I opened one of Bunty's books, just mechanically to see what it was about, and these words caught my eye: "May God deny thee peace and give thee glory."

Well, that was enough to go on with! It was, I discovered, a wish with which the old Spanish knights were accustomed to greet each other, and it occurred, somewhat irrelevantly, in a book which I did not think of as inviting. But that sentence stayed with me all day long.

There was no "glory" in me – that I very well knew – but into that interior-conversation sprang a line from one of Samuel Rutherford's letters: "God careth not what poor stuff He maketh glory of."

All this time one part of me was on-the-listen. One of Mr. Hazeldean's young men came for the grocery order; the laundry man came; the electric light man came; and each time I hurried to the door thinking it must be our evacuees.

Early in the afternoon I had a surprise. Mrs. Nonesuch came. She took the tea-cloths I was washing out of my hands, and began to wash them herself, while she explained that she was situated just as we were. Her expected visitors had not come.

She said she would rather be at work than sticking about at home being miserable – her neighbour would soon let her know if she were wanted – and she entreated me to go up at once and take my usual afternoon's rest.

We had just made ourselves some tea when the gas men came to fix the cooker, and those gas men were our old friends, Self and Mate, who have obliged us so often and who know us so well. I left them drinking tea with Mrs. Nonesuch. With the greatest thankfulness I went upstairs, lay flat upon my back, and began to count my blessings.

## OH, CAN IT BE IN TIMES LIKE THESE!

Now England's fields are past their mowing;
Now England's scabiouses are showing;
Her butterflies are on the thyme,
And bees hum glorias to the lime;
Her raspberries redden, and her plums
Wax plummier every day that comes!

Now from each English kitchen swells
Delectable and fruity smells;
Jugs of new milk have yellow tops;
Now there are sales in English shops;
Now minnows swim in every pool,
And all the bairns come home from school.

Oh, can it be in times like these
Death will come flying overseas?

# LET US BE THE PEOPLE OF THE PLOUGH!

Let us be the people of the plough again –
The people of the plough!
Let us bend our backs and toil
For the sake of English soil,
While the peewits follow – follow –
Over English hill and hollow;
Plough until the good earth stirs
And the miracle occurs;
Sow until the green wheat springing
Sets the English larks all singing,
And the old sea winds come blowing
Through the old moist English air;
Until English barns o'erflowing
Say there's bread enough to spare!

Shame on our black-coated pride
With grey cities satisfied,
When the English countryside
Cries aloud from old and furrowed
English meadows! Even now
Let us be the people of the plough again –
The people of the plough!

## Chapter Three

### THE VILLAGE ENTERTAINS STRANGERS

DURING THE NEXT FEW DAYS OUR HOUSE WAS THE scene of great activity on the part of Self and Mate. They fitted pipes, fixed up the cooker and installed a separate meter.

Self thought we should have done better to have provided a gas-ring for our evacuees. "They won't need a cooker, Mam," said he. "All they wants is a tin opener – they lives out of tins!"

Self had already made Mrs. Nonesuch's blood run cold with his tales of the doings of "them ladies from London!" He had been called in to every house of any size in the district. He hinted darkly that what he had seen and heard over the week-end at the Colonel's, at the Doctor's, and at *Mavoureen* would fill a book.

When Self and Mate had gone, some of these happenings, kindly edited by Mrs. Nonesuch, were related to me – and, truly, the circumstances seemed appalling. Mrs. Nonesuch stated with conviction that if she were required to harbour such folk in her house she would immediately go raving mad!

For three weeks Mrs. Nonesuch and I went on expecting the invasion of our homes. We lived as it were from hand to mouth – with our everyday things all crowded together in the kitchen, and nowhere to keep our table linen.

Certain articles began to creep back into the china pantry

"just till the mothers arrive". The vessels we had appointed for their use had got pushed into cupboards, or were reabsorbed into household use again.

One evening, at a meeting concerning the distribution of gas-masks, I met Mrs. Wills. She was up to her neck in Village matters, and was almost worn to death with arranging and changing billets.

I said: "Oh! Mrs. Wills, our mothers have not arrived."

She replied: "There were not enough to go round. I hope you were not disappointed?"

I am ashamed to say it, but I went home harbouring feelings of relief. For the time being we had a reprieve – yet, if our turn came later we were not unprepared. Thoughts of what we had done which need not have been done, and of what we had spent unnecessarily, were all swallowed up in feelings of release. We took our dust sheets from the dark place under the stairs, and put them tidily in their own drawer, and Mrs. Nonesuch did her ironing in the sitting-room again.

Hitler seemed in no hurry to attack Britain, yet Britain, including our small corner of it, was at sixes and sevens.

A village, being a small community, is rather like a family. It is almost impossible for any member of it to do anything in secret. Every action is subjected to the most severe scrutiny, and as things of a surprising nature are always happening, we are never at a loss for conversation. As a matter of fact we do not like too many interesting things to happen at once. We prefer to come to them one by one that we may extract the full flavour from each. Such events are turned inside out and upside down – viewed and reviewed from every possible and impossible angle – and opinions are freely expressed.

Before the war we had enjoyed a running series of excitements which, after the manner of Bateman's celebrated sketches, might have been entitled:

The Maid who Addressed Her Mistress as Dear.

The Strange Lady who Kissed the Policeman.

The Missing Daughter who was Followed to Gretna Green.

These had been very fruitful subjects for gossip, but now they took subordinate places. Only one topic was worthy of exploitation, and that topic was – the strangers within our gates.

Behind every darkened window-pane at that delectable and elastic hour known as tea-time, women's heads were bent together relating fresh enormities perpetrated by the aliens. Eyebrows rose to astonishing heights, hands exhausted themselves with frequent gestures, and lips were contorted into curious shapes, but all were expressive of dismay.

The Village which had stood on tip-toe with outstretched arms, anxious to succour those distressed sisters fleeing from fire and sudden death, was going through a stage of disillusionment. Excitement had given way to everydayness. Entertaining strangers, who could not by any stretch of imagination be described as angels, showed signs of becoming a wearisome performance.

Dejected-looking women with prams, and strange hair, were seen wandering up and down our steep lanes. They complained bitterly of the absence of cinemas and shops. There was not, they said, even an air-raid shelter. One of them stated solemnly that she did not want to see another green tree as long as she lived. These, women were most of them small and sharp featured, very quick at the uptake, noisy in laughter, and with – to us – a strange intonation in their speech.

They had been suddenly transplanted from their usual environment; they had none of the amenities which had in the past kept them happy and interested from day to day – no cheap stores, no street stalls, no fried-fish shops. They found the country food "very dear" compared with that of the cities. It was true they could now obtain milk straight from the cow, and vegetables straight from the earth. But these quick little women liked such things better out of a tin.

Why should they buy raw fish and have to fry it? Or raw vegetables and have to cook them? Why should they make milk puddings and have to wait while they baked – when a tin-opener could do nearly all their work for them, and made next to no washing-up?

It was not easy for the Village to feel any sympathy with such an outlook, and Mrs. Briggs, an elderly widow who had a boy and his sister billeted upon her, went to Mrs. Wills one evening with a sorrowful tale.

"They keeps asking me for biscuits which I haven't got, and for tinned milk which I don't hold with. I've brought up eight," said Mrs. Briggs tearfully, "and made 'em eat what was on their plates, but these have got me beat, Mam, and there it is."

Mrs. Wills sympathized with the difficulties, remarked on the greatly improved appearance of the children, and sent her away with a flush of gratification on her cheeks. Yes, she would try again, and maybe in time she would get them into the way of eating nice greens and proper gravy.

To Maxwell and his wife Mrs. Wills sent three little girls who addressed then as Uncle and Auntie, and made themselves thoroughly at home. Mrs. Maxwell mothered them, and every week a letter of gratitude was received from the children's parents.

Of course, everything was not plain sailing. The little girls had their small accidents and illnesses; washing for them, and cooking for them, took considerable time. Mrs. Maxwell was kept busy ministering to ear-aches, tooth-aches and sore throats, and Maxwell often went down in the night to get the little evacuees a drink of warm milk, or a biscuit or two to send them off to sleep again.

Mrs. Berringer, who lives at the big house opposite and who employs Maxwell when Michael does not want him, was not quite so fortunate. She took in a stout, loud-voiced woman with two boys. Mrs. Berringer supplied vegetables and allowed numerous privileges, but the visitor intimated that she quite thought the Government would "find" everything for her.

When it was explained that the butcher and the grocer must be paid for the goods fetched, the stout woman with a great flow of language blamed Mrs. Berringer for the Government's deceptiveness! The two boys trampled over the begonias and poked the tame rabbit with sticks. They made queer faces at the cook, and spoke insolently to her; and then one Sunday morning, when the family were at church, the stout woman's husband arrived with a car and took her and the two boys away.

Mrs. Nonesuch was often in request to help to receive newcomers at the Village Hall. A great lover of children, she was an ideal welcomer of the shy and the homesick. She told me many stories of the pitiful little suitcases she unpacked, which contained badly washed and shrunken underwear sadly in need of mending; of pretty and engaging mites who were quickly pounced upon by foster mothers; of belligerent and none too clean little persons who were with difficulty provided with billets.

It was not an easy thing to be a billeting officer, and I view with veneration the people who undertake this difficult task. I think that out of all of them Mr. Pedlar must be given the palm for showing tact, self-giving, and sheer goodness of heart when confronted with strange and harassing circumstances. No one knows better than he the curious dilemmas which may quite suddenly arise when persons totally unknown to one another have to live under the same roof, and often in the same rooms. Mr. Pedlar has been fetched at all sorts of odd times to deal with queer customers, and to smooth down indignant house-mothers. He has been obliged to read the Riot Act as loudly, and as fiercely, as his kindly nature will let him.

This he was compelled to do in the case of Erbie's father.

Erbie's mother and Erbie – an infant of fifteen months – were placed with Mrs. Tubbs. Erbie's mother went out one morning and did not return. She was seen boarding the London train.

Erbie's father, who appeared to have made a habit of stealing motor-cars, was in prison for his last offence, and out of pity for "the little dear" Mrs. Tubbs agreed to look after Erbie. She had been doing this for some time, when late one night Erbie's father arrived in a car – also stolen – in search of his wife and child.

He was the worse for drink, and he was very abusive when he discovered his wife was not there. He insisted that Mrs. Tubbs must put him up. Mrs. Tubbs sent for Mr. Pedlar, who took Erbie's father in hand, and after administering the sobering influence of a strong cup of tea, miraculously found a room for him. The next morning he took Erbie's father to make his apologies to Mrs. Tubbs, and the situation which had seemed insoluble cleared up.

But many of Mr. Pedlar's experiences have been less sordid and much happier than this. One evening in the late autumn he took an elderly woman to her new home. She was to stay with Mrs. Thorn, and Mrs. Thorn's house stands in a lovely garden. Carrying her small bundle for her, Mr. Pedlar opened the gate and the elderly evacuee stepped inside. She looked around her with rapture. Gazing at the Michaelmas daisies and at the brilliant dahlias she exclaimed: "This here is just like my first place of service."

The old lady's contentment increased when she discovered that Mrs. Thorn had now only one general helper, and that there were plenty of jobs to be done. This elderly stranger rubbed brasses, polished silver, did a good deal of washing-up, and made herself responsible for preparing the vegetables. Each time she sees Mr. Pedlar, she says the same thing with the same expansive smile: "Ain't it lovely for me? This is just like being in service again."

There was, I remember, some perturbation among the ladies who did the welcoming when out of one of the buses drawn up in the narrow lane stepped a woman whose face was the colour of parchment, and who carried twin babies in her shawl. Twins! They were eleven weeks old, and two other children, Rosie and Ettie, were holding on to their mother's skirts and sniffing.

Who was there who could and who would put up five?

The mother was all but exhausted by the bus journey, and she drank tea with loud gulps of thankfulness. Mrs. Wills' comely face was puckered up with the problem of where to place them, when Miss Ventnor and Miss Watts offered to take them in.

The kindness of these two friends cannot be properly estimated until one remembers that they are two not-so-young gentlewomen who came to our Village a year before the war, for the sake of quiet, after years of unrelenting work in the mission field. Their house is one of those inconvenient places where steps and stairs abound, and which only by extreme tidiness can be kept in any sort of order. Miss Watts and Miss Ventnor gave the mother of the twins the lower floor of their house. They possessed only one spare bed, and for that first night they were put to great shifts to find sufficient bedding and to manage sufficient food, for it was early-closing day when our grocer shuts up at one o'clock.

Rosie and Ettie lifted up their voices in a wail, and dropped off to sleep while Miss Watts was trying to wash them. Miss Ventnor got the mother into bed with a hot bottle, and put the screaming twins into her arms because there was nowhere else to put them. But drinks of warm milk worked wonders, and about midnight the two hostesses went with thankfulness to their own beds.

The tale of the twins spread far and wide, and the heart of the Village was moved with compassion. Wool coats and wool bootees were given in abundance. Almost every woman who had baby clothes put away found something for the service of the twins. The mother wearing a blue coat and hat (given by Mrs. Wills) began to push a pram (given by Mrs. Brendon) up to the shop. Rosie and Ettie in red tam-o'-shanters and leggings (knitted by Mrs. Ellison) appeared at Sunday School.

Miss Ventnor and Miss Watts spoke eloquently of the mother's gratitude, and of the increasing prettiness and responsiveness of the twins. Of their own discomfort, want of peace and privacy they said nothing. These two ladies interpreted to the Village something which found a lodging place in its heart.

Indeed, it seemed impossible to set a limit to the goodness of spirit shown by Miss Ventnor and her friend. The mother of the twins pined for her two other children, and her hostesses suggested they should be sent for. Eventually the woman's husband put in an appearance, and he, too, took up his abode with them. He was a handy kind of man, and soon we heard he was doing the garden, mending door-handles and putting washers on taps.

After a while he got regular work in Broadwater and moved there with his family – a very different family from the one which had first arrived in the Village. The twins so fat and so lively, able to chuckle and to make happy bubbling noises; Ettie and Rosie chattering and singing; and the mother herself had regained a sprightliness of which she showed no sign that dour afternoon when she stepped out of the jolting bus.

Thinking of this family reminds me of the history of the seven.

They began by being only two. Emma, red-haired, with shrewd inquisitive eyes and an air of never being gainsaid, was evacuated with her little boy of four to the little old town of Broadwater. Unknown to the authorities, she returned to London and fetched her sister Maud, and Maud's two little girls. Emma also collected her father and mother, a knowing old couple, seventyish or so.

These she brought back to the little old town, where the authorities groaned. Emma had been evacuated under the Government scheme, but these relations of hers had not, and accommodation could not be found for them. So the seven were put in the Town Hall for the night. The next day the Evacuation Officer telephoned to our Mrs. Wills inquiring whether accommodation could be found in the Village for seven. After some scouting round Mrs. Wills decided that it could.

When Mrs. Nonesuch returned as usual to get our supper we learned that Emma and Emma's little boy were billeted upon her. She would have to hurry home to get supper for them. Maud and her two children were settled in at Miss Moxam's, and Grandpa and Grandma were lodged up Corkscrew Hill next door to the Maxwells.

That all sounded very well. We knew Mrs. Nonesuch would do her part, and good-natured Miss Moxam is the farmeress of the Village. Her cows are the cleanest, silkiest-coated creatures and we thought Maud exceedingly fortunate to be sent there.

Mrs. Nonesuch arrived the next morning, and Bunty and I leaned over the banisters and said: "Well?"

She looked up from rubbing the hall and began to laugh.

"I got their supper all ready and kept it hot until ten o'clock, and then Emma came to the door crying, to say she wasn't coming – all the seven of them were spending the night at the Village Hall."

Mrs. Nonesuch began polishing the front door knocker, knocking it with a kind of accompaniment while she talked.

"Emma didn't like her father and mother (knock-knock) being away up the hill, so she went and fetched them and their luggage down to Miss Moxam's (knock-knock), and she took her own luggage and her boy there as well.

"Miss Moxam was not there at the time, but Emma had everything figured out (knock-knock). They would all seven live in one room, and be no trouble to anyone, but Miss Moxam came home just as they were dragging the bedclothes on to the floor, and Miss Moxam went straight to Mrs. Wills, and she came down very upset indeed, and she took the seven to the Village Hall, and they had to sleep on the floor, as they said they wouldn't be separated, and there was nowhere else."

We felt very sorry for this united and distracted family. We also felt very sorry for Mrs. Wills, who had had so much trouble and had not given satisfaction. Then the almost miraculous happened. Mrs. Fernley offered her furnished cottage for the use of the seven.

We – by which I mean the Village – gasped to think of their

good fortune. Some people could always fall on their feet. Some persons clearly had been born under a lucky star. For Mrs. Fernley's cottage was not just a cottage – it was *the* cottage.

In a village which has many beautiful homes, each in its own setting, Mrs. Fernley's home is something quite apart. Standing high upon the hillside, its foundations set quite literally upon rock, *The Chantry* has a beauty which is clear-cut and austere. Cars cannot approach very near to it – visitors must climb the rocky path which gets steeper as it ascends. The garden has to be entirely a rock garden, there is nothing softening nor accommodating, no pandering to easy ways. But when, more or less winded, the climber stands at the top and sees the view across the Frome valley, he knows why the monks chose this place as a haven where they might turn their eyes away from the works of man, and look continually upon the handiwork of God.

Within a stone's throw of *The Chantry* stands the cottage. It had been a garden house for the young Fernleys, and a most delectable playhouse, but on the outbreak of war Mrs. Fernley, in collaboration with Mr. Flower, had the cottage made habitable with special amenities for bombed-out mothers and their children. The pretty china, the lino, the washable rugs, and the beds with dainty floral bedspreads and pink blankets were the envy of the Village.

Of this cottage the seven evacuees were very glad to take possession, and Mrs. Fernley who is young, charming and beautiful as well, acted the part of Lady Bountiful. Vegetables, cooked dinners, clothes for the children and countless other benefits were showered upon the seven.

Grandpa, who appears to have been rather a humorous old man, began to do a little weeding in the garden. He and his Missis might have been the originals of one of George Belcher's sketches. Grandpa had wild hair and a moustache, baggy trousers and a wink. Grandma liked to sit by the cottage fire with her large arms folded over her capacious bodice.

Mr. Fernley paid Grandpa for working in the garden. The Village said he received a pound a week to do a little how and when he liked, and stared half-enviously to think of such good fortune.

But in spite of everything that was done the seven were not

happy. One would have thought that they were, as the Village said, "on velvet", but the Fernleys found when they got up one morning that the family had thrown up the sponge and were gone. The Village was not their home and never would be.

All these weeks the war against Poland had been proceeding – said the German High Command – according to plan; and that plan included the most barbaric and dastardly attack upon Warsaw. The Poles, in spite of valiant resistance, were crushed. We did not know then how ruthless, how devastating, how invincible mechanized forces could be against a people ill-prepared to meet them.

In the late autumn the Queen of Holland and the King of the Belgians issued a joint peace plea to the belligerent powers.

Those who clung to the idea of peace before Christmas were disappointed. The war went on, and the Village, like the rest of the country, was in for a difficult time. Evacuees kept coming and going. The little houses and the big houses were alike invaded. Those who were not harbouring Government evacuees were giving refuge to relations from danger zones.

The Village had never been so crowded; never had there been so many harassed housewives; nor so many cooks giving notice. Circumstances were very hard all round in that first winter of the war – hard for mistresses and hard for maids, hard for householders, and hard for the strangers suddenly bundled in to share the hearthstone.

I have been asking myself why it was that with so many good intentions, and with so much real sacrifice, things in the main turned out so awkwardly for so many people. Part of the trouble was, I think, that nothing in the least sensational happened.

There was no sudden air attack upon London. There were no breath-taking fearsome odours of peardrops or geraniums to justify the troublesomeness of carrying gas-masks. Our leaders counselled us to look upon this interlude as the lull before the storm. They entreated us to remember that Hitler's attack upon the British Isles, air-borne or sea-borne or both together, might occur at any moment, but in spite of these warnings there was, on the part of the evacuees, a determined trek towards home.

When the Village was almost deserted again, when the little

houses and the big houses had only their own families to shelter, there was a distinct feeling of relief. But there was something else as well – the Village felt a disposition to recall the good points of the departed guests.

It had been a time of revelation and heart-searching. The Government had asked a hard thing. It is not easy to share one's own fireside indefinitely with anybody, but those who were least able – so it seemed – were the ones most willing to show the true Samaritan spirit. In that season of testing our Village, so easily moved to compassion and also impatience, learned lessons which could not have been learned in any other way.

There were other changes which came to the Village. Our beautiful Hydro, which had attracted many visitors to our valley, and several old-fashioned family residences passed into the possession of a business firm known as the Belfry Road Building Society. These were houses shut away and almost hidden from the world by their own lordly trees. They were built by the prosperous merchants of Victorian days for the accommodation of large families. They were roomy houses where a staff of servants made it possible for guests to be entertained; where a governess ruled over the schoolroom, and neatly uniformed nannies presided over capacious nurseries. In such houses the pleasant and ceremonious rites of living in moderate "style" could be indulged.

Those days were over long ago. Staffs dwindled in many cases to one solitary retainer. Those persons who had kept two maids had now to manage with daily help. Ways of life were simplified wherever possible, but even such drastic changes were not enough, and the old houses had to be sold.

Where one had been accustomed to enter and walk up the drive, sure of a welcome, it was a little saddening to see at the entrance gates: *Strictly Private. No Admission Except on Business.* It was saddening to know that the lovely old upstairs rooms were being partitioned into cubicles, with bathrooms on every landing; the conservatories denuded of flowers and converted into offices, or into living accommodation for office workers, who soon arrived – a band of gay-hearted happy young people with something metropolitan in their clothes, and in their manners.

After a short season of inquiry and doubtfulness the Village gave evidence that it had taken the newcomers to its heart, for it began to call them the "Belfry-Roaders", and their doings were watched with interest. Indeed, when vacancies occurred in the office staff, a goodly number of village belles hastened to be admitted to the Belfry.

Often, after I was in bed at night, I heard footsteps going along the lane which borders our garden, and sometimes, pleasant lilting voices were raised in song. The Belfry-Roaders going home, I thought sleepily to myself, and by now they did not seem like the voices of strangers. Almost imperceptibly these young people had slipped into the life of the Village.

# ENGLAND CALLING TO HER CHILDREN

England – England – England calling,
England entering war's dark cloud;
England calling to her children
With a solemn cry and loud:

I have nursed you! I have given
All you know of earth or heaven.
Now, I look to you with calmness,
Confident am I and proud!
You, my own, and very own,
Of my flesh and of my bone,
You have nothing if you lose me –
I am nothing left alone.

Up, my daughters! Up, my sons!
Up, my gently nurtured ones!
Taste no more of ease or pleasure
Till the foe is overthrown.
This is England – England calling
To her own, her very own!

# THE ANSWER OF ENGLAND'S CHILDREN

If we have been too slow or too unmindful,
England, to repay our mighty debt,
Forgive us – and then ask of us the hard things;
The hard unthought-of things made harder yet!

Ask us for our dreams and you shall take them;
Ask us for our life blood or our treasure;
Use our young slim bodies till you break them;
Take our working hours and take our leisure.

Not for nothing did you travail, England,
Bringing forth your children to the birth;
Not for nothing have you taught your children
How to cast a girdle round the earth.

We have nothing, England, if we lose you;
You have nothing, England, left alone;
We are England, now – and always – England!
England's own and Very Own!

*Chapter Four*

## THE TURN OF THE YEAR

THE YEAR 1939 WORE TO ITS CLOSE AND WE ENTERED upon 1940. This was the devastating and stressful year when the map of Europe changed its face and the whole world looked on, wondering with indrawn breath what new atrocity this audacious and maddenly successful enemy would spring upon it.

After Poland came the long "pause" which kept us guessing. Where and when would the next offensive begin? Anglo-French cordiality was at its height. A British parliamentary delegation had visited France; twelve members of the French Chamber of Deputies came to England. There was "an atmosphere of absolute frankness and mutual confidence".

We remembered Marshal Foch, and we remembered the Maginot Line, and to many of us this New Year seemed to promise hopeful things. When we had waited a little longer and had prepared a little more, we and the French, having set our armies in array, would meet this undeniably mighty foe and give him back stroke for stroke and blow for blow.

War work spelt with two capital W's now became the chief activity of all English cities, and our Roman City was no exception. It was then, before we had to register, that those who employed young girls began to feel the pinch. Housemaids, hairdressers, shop assistants, nannies, mannequins and young married women began falling over each other to do war work. I am afraid that the not-so-young section of our Village could not help giving one or two small hastily suppressed sighs at the new turn of events.

Elderly gentlewomen, who had been waited on all their lives, had to rise early in those dark and bitter winter mornings, to light fires and take early tea and breakfasts to less able-bodied members of the household.

The grandmothers of the Village came into their own, and in some cases into more than their own. No longer were they looked upon as fussy and interfering back numbers – they had become too useful to be ignored. Who but a grandmother could be expected to take charge of small grandchildren so that daughters and daughters-in-law could skip off to the Roman City?

These young women thoroughly enjoyed themselves. Released from the drudgery of housekeeping; dressed in smart costumes; hatless, but with immaculately permed hair they ran, swinging their neat attaché-cases, for the eight o'clock train. They did not return until evening when their tea-supper was put before them, their day's work done.

The grey-haired grandmothers were left to wrestle with house-cleaning, cooking, the difficulties of rationed shopping, and the constant care of children. It is hard work pushing a pram up our steep hills but the grandmothers did it, though some of them thought the situation "a bit thick", and Mrs. Wendover astonished Kitty, her daughter-in-law, by going away one Friday evening and not returning until Sunday night.

Kitty was dumbfounded and dismayed. She was a dark-eyed, vivacious little person who had caught the fancy of Mrs. Wendover's boy Jock, had lured him to London and married him. Now it was a rare joke for her and the baby to be evacuated to our Village, and billeted on her mother-in-law – until that mother-in-law showed plainly that she had no intention of being a door-mat for Kitty to wipe her *suède* shoes upon.

It was an angry and outraged Kitty who joined her friends at the station on Monday morning. All the way to their offices she was telling them how "she" went off, and never even had Kitty's tea ready, nor the baby put to bed. Kitty had to keep things going all day Saturday and Sunday, Kitty had to cook for her father-in-law, who liked his food and did not mind criticizing the cooking, and Kitty had to look after her own small child of eighteen months whose hands were into everything.

Kitty was sniffing and coughing with a heavy cold owing, she said, to the wind cutting her like a knife every time she had to go across the yard for a shovelful of coal, which her father-in-law had accused her of burning in waste, and Kitty supposed he wanted her to freeze in her chair.

Concerning the weather Kitty had used no exaggeration. In this part of England we have the reputation of possessing a singularly soft climate, but the winter of 1939-40 was almost arctic. Frost, ice and snow gripped the green countryside and held it in an icy grasp. The newspapers, if they came at all, were delivered in the afternoon and Mr. Nonesuch, who drives the bread van, frequently did not reach home till midnight. He had had to walk miles on the tops of hedges to deliver bread to out-of-the-way farms, and to outlying cottages.

The wind made a kind of *Luftwaffe* of its own going down our valley. It had that harp-like note which always betokens north wind and snow, and John was much concerned about coal. How to secure sufficient fuel to keep us warm was to him an ever-recurring problem. He entreated us to be as careful as possible; to learn to manipulate the Ideal boiler so that it did not roar itself away and incidentally fur the pipes. He made careful calculations concerning the contents of the cellar, and drew up a time-table allowing so much coal and coke per day.

Going up the road I met a lorry loaded with logs and hailed by the driver, who stated that he would sell the load – cheap. I bought the lot there and then. When Michael heard the price he drew in his mouth, and went on stacking the logs in the shed.

Bunty was also waylaid by an Irishman with a Somerset accent who was selling peat. Lured by a nostalgia for the Emerald Isle, she parted with twenty-five good English shillings to secure a hundred sods of it.

The Day the Coal Came – a whole load of it – was a good day for us. The two coalmen with grimy, perspiring faces tramped down the cellar steps and hurled each sackful into the dark damp depths with a thud which reverberated through the house. They were regaled with cups of sweetened tea and hunches of cake – regardless!

Through all this the Finns were fighting magnificently against the Russians. Our thoughts about Russia were as cold and as clear-cut as her own ice. Under our very noses she had made a pact with Germany, for which many blamed our own Government, and she had descended on Poland. Now, she had attacked Finland.

We were all of us angry with Russia and grieved for the Finns. For Finland at that time we had the greatest respect – was she not hard-working, and was she not the only country in Europe who had continued to pay her debts to America? Some of our newspapers told us we ought to send immediate assistance to Finland, and Finland herself appealed to America for help. In the end an expeditionary force of British and French was prepared, but Norwegian neutrality stood in the way and it was never sent. It was left for a small band of volunteers, led by a certain gallant American colonel, to strike the only blow which was struck for Finland.

How could we dream that within a few months a state of war would exist between Great Britain and Finland, and that Russia would be our ally?

After the long hard frost had broken we had torrents of rain – cold rain which harrowed the bones. Then frost had another innings until the roads were like glass, and each morning John and Bunty slid most of the way to the station. Michael, muffled to the ears, had to sweep a path to the front door and to the back door, and to strew that path with ashes. Mrs. Nonesuch arrived each morning with lurid stories of tumbles into snowdrifts and of lorries snow-logged on the main road.

Like many another in the Village I was weather-bound. From the windows I could see the grandeur of the trees, each branch encased in ice like the branches of a glass chandelier. The cold was really fierce in its onslaught – it whipped the ears and the fingers. A correspondent once sent me a pair of mittens upon which I looked with wonder! Now I wore them with thankfulness, day and night, calling down blessings on the donor's name. I took to bed socks, I took to a woollen shoulder-cape – and, still, was far from warm.

The fire – and we are accustomed to keep a large one – seemed to make little impression upon the icy atmosphere. We ate our supper at a small gate-legged table in the drawing-room. We tried to listen to Hitler's birthday speech, but a very little of that frenzied voice went a long way and we were glad to click the obliging button and have the silence back again.

Those speeches, so hysterical and uncontrolled as they seemed to us, made us wonder what the German people really thought. If one could judge by the applause, they must have called forth warm approval from the listeners.

Yet the Germans – as we used to know them – were a highly intelligent people. Not very quick at the uptake, perhaps – and their men had something arrogant and patronizing in their treatment of women. We looked upon them as painstaking, industrious, with a flair for mechanisms – and something else. They were capable of an outgoing of spirit which English folk, taken as a whole, do not possess.

If German people were like they used to be – or like we thought them once – how could they listen to and applaud the bombastic Adolf? Thinkers tell us that nations as well as individuals have souls, that nations as well as individuals are faced with the two-way choice. They must go after the highest they know, or decide to follow something lower. In heiling Hitler, the Germans were heiling themselves, for Hitler – with his lust for power, his aggression and his bombast – is their representative man; and him they choose to follow, just as they followed Frederick the Great, Bismarck, and Kaiser William.

I was alone a great deal that winter for Mrs. Nonesuch was increasingly engaged in voluntary work. Someone was always seizing upon her to help assemble gas-masks, to collect the hospital subscriptions, or to assist with washing-up at the canteen, for we now had soldiers quartered in the Village.

Their arrival was marked by a great clattering and rumbling of lorries, full of merry-faced lads in battle-dress going full speed ahead down the precipitous roadway, which abounds in concealed turnings and cantankerous corners and for a great part of the way has no footpath. The big empty house known as *The Lodge*, recently vacated by the Major, was their headquarters, and the secluded country road, which led to it, became the scene of hilarious activity.

In spite of the prescribed black-out, in spite of the vigilance of wardens, lights constantly flared from the windows of *The Lodge*. The lads who came home late at night came singing from the station, causing sighs, and otherwise, from the Village which was already in bed and trying to snatch at those precious hours before midnight said to be so necessary for health and beauty.

In the day time small contingents of soldiers drilled in the road outside *The Lodge*. They stood presenting arms, and forming threes till the sergeant's exasperated "Quick-march" was followed by tramping feet in strict precision.

Mrs. Nonesuch, whose house was close by, said the canteen was very popular. They could never cut enough sandwiches, nor make enough coffee, yet she thought their meals were ample and well cooked. The cook-house was in the yard down our dark lane. Often, as Mrs. Nonesuch passed just before eight o'clock, she smelt their breakfast bacon, and thought how fortunate they were not to be rationed, when we had to make ours go the week round whether it would or not.

She had a soft spot in her heart for the soldiers. She was always knitting for them; asking them into her own house for supper, because they were away from home and she thought how glad she would be for someone to do it for her brothers.

Many who had rooms to spare had officers in them, and they were frequently accompanied by their wives. Mrs. Trent had two non-commissioned officers, and she often alluded proudly to "My Sergeants!"

When Mrs. Trent's sergeants had gone she let a bedroom with attendance to an officer's wife – a good-looking woman, thirty-fivish, who liked to sit by Mrs. Trent's sitting-room fire, and to use Mrs. Trent's sewing-machine.

It was understood that the officer would "come when he could". Before long he found he could come every night; then he found he could arrive in time for supper; he even managed to come occasionally in time for lunch. Sometimes he was accompanied by his batman, who found it very pleasant to be sitting in Mrs. Trent's kitchen and chattering to Mrs. Trent's young daughter.

Mrs. Trent said little, but presently she intimated that certain relatives from danger areas would soon be requiring all her lettable rooms; the officer's wife had to seek other accommodation, and Mrs. Trent saw the officer and his batman no more.

I was obliged to be rather a keeper-at-home, but Bunty's leisure hours were filled up with Nursing and with A.R.P. Lectures, and I began to wonder what my own work ought to be.

Surely, there was some definite task somewhere which would be helpful to England, and which was within the reach of persons like myself. John told me to remember my handicap, and I told him I was more than anxious to forget it. Was I to spend the rest of my life keeping up fires, sweeping up crumbs, and putting away the day-by-day accumulation of muddles?

John looked unconvinced but he said no more, and when I came to think of it I saw that a very large part of my life had been spent doing odds and ends. I have never had anything which could be dignified by the name of a "life-work". Even my writing has been done between whiles, with all kinds of interruptions cropping up. This way of going on did not seem to be nearly as useful as going out at nine to some vital task, and returning at six after a well-spent day.

Many women of uncertain age now began to take jobs as book-keepers and accountants. Some of them helped in the nearby hospital, and Miss Burdock opened a private school for children who had been suddenly sent to relatives, or had come with their mothers to sojourn in the Village.

In the meantime, and while my mind was straying round various ideas, I began going to Mrs. Wills's Working Party. Every woman who could guide a needle, and some who couldn't, sat in the Church Room on Friday afternoons, sewing long seams in garments known as "helpless cases" and making dressing gowns for wounded soldiers. Mrs. Wills did the cutting out, and was adviser-in-chief to poor tools like myself; who did not know how to fit a gusset and could not be trusted to make button-holes. Each member of the Working Party contributed twopence a week which was collected in a saucer. This was to pay for the use of the gas-fire; any surplus in funds went for the purchase of Service wool.

It was very pleasant to be there. An atmosphere of friendliness was in that small Church Room. No time was wasted, and though, of course, we talked, the work went on just the same.

Mrs. Ellison, whose exquisite skill as a needlewoman must have been an asset to Mrs. Wills, was always present, and so was Mrs. Vicary who also came from London.

Mrs. Brendon, whose house was full of grandchildren, officiated with a sewing-machine; the Rectoress came whenever she could, and nearly everyone arrived with some garment which had been completed at home during the week – and threw it down triumphantly on the table before Mrs. Wills.

We were all so much in earnest that our coming together might have resulted in a deadly serious convocation if it had not been for the presence of Miss Katie Bannister. Miss Katie provided our Working Party with the lighter side – she had always some brisk comment to make on every subject under the sun. Her shrewd humorous face reminded one of the accepted portrait of Jane Austen. Miss Katie had the same round rather prominent eyes and confident bearing. Nothing escaped her.

She and her elderly maid lived in a roomy old house. When an attempt was made to billet children with them, it was said in the village that Mr. Pedlar, though a brave and valorous man, literally quailed under the lash of Miss Katie Bannister's tongue.

"How many did you think to place here, Mr. Pedlar?" The Billeting Officer said gently that according to the number of rooms he proposed to send eight.

"And who, Mr. Pedlar, is going to cook for them, and wash for them, and iron for them? Not I, Mr. Pedlar. I should most likely murder the children before they had been here a week."

"Then, perhaps," said Mr. Pedlar, "we had better send a teacher with them."

Miss Katie replied that perhaps he had, provided she was not to be held responsible for the safety of the teacher. In the end Mr. Pedlar retired discomfited, and Miss Bannister's house remained free from invasion.

At the Working Party Miss Katie led the conversation about the difficulties which had already arisen, and of those which might be before us. The utility of gas-rings came under discussion. Mrs. Banks had one fixed on her landing, and the members of her household used it in turns to make themselves early tea; their respective trays and tea pots stood in a row on the floor, and Mr. Banks, getting up in the night because Mrs. Banks smelt something burning, had stepped into them.

Miss Katie Bannister said: "Faugh!"

Mrs. Brendon used an electric kettle from a switch close to her bed, but Miss Burdock thought it extremely likely that gas and electricity would both be cut off; as an emergency measure she had bought an oil stove and a small drum of oil.

I was just making a mental note to write to our ironmonger immediately, when Miss Laylaw said she had a great belief in methylated spirit. She had invested in a small gadget for boiling a kettle and found its convenience beyond price.

Miss Katie thought those who used such appliances would all be blown up in their beds.

Matches had become scarce and we had most of us returned to the habit practised by our grandparents of making spills from old letters. Mrs. Wills thought we ought not to burn paper at any time, and she advocated a fusilier which was worked with flints. When I went to town I bought one – the price of which had recently been 1s. 3d. had gone up to 4s. 9d., plus the flints; and soon there was no flints to plus, for they were unobtainable.

Mrs. Ventnor's friend and house-mate had heard there would be a shortage of soap and candles. I decided to get in a few extra of each. As soon as I got home, I mounted the china-pantry dresser to get down three ancient candlesticks. I meant to put a candle and a box of matches in each and deposit the three in the hall cupboard. If sudden oblivion overtook us, I could find my way there in the dark. Just at that unlucky moment, when I was stepping from dresser to chair, John came home. He stood looking at me with that half-puzzled, half-indulgent look which he keeps for me alone.

"What do you think you're doing?"

I told him about the oil, and about the methylated spirit, and about the candles, and about the soap.

He said: "Don't be a panic purchaser. At present we have gas *and* electricity. If that fails we must cook by an open fire again."

"But," said I, "suppose we have no coal?"

He replied: "Then we'll chop up the piano. Nobody ever plays it now we have the wireless."

One day before January was out I saw that the buds of the copper beech had tips of light upon them; and beneath the copper beech, between its green knees, winter aconites had put out their golden heads.

On the hilltop, which lies opposite and is many feet higher than our hill, I could see the white horse and the brown horse going patiently up and down the steep field turning over the earth.

The man behind the plough was their friend and not their tyrant. He was a representative man – that cheery fellow, the English ploughman, upon whose labours we must now more than ever learn to depend. Over a million and a half more acres were to be tilled during that first spring of the war. Snow and ice had delayed it, but now the farmer was at it full tilt. Everywhere one went, on foot, by car or by train, large expanses of the good English earth were upturned to the beneficent sky. After this came the seed sowing.

I remembered how, in the old gabled town where we used to live, Rogationtide was observed with some ceremony. The "church", led by the vicar, went out into the fields around Clover Close and, looking up towards the hill on which the town was built, asked for blessing on the springing corn. Indeed, it was noticeable just at this point how Everybody's Prayer seemed to come into its own. *Give us this day our daily bread* was a vital petition, while *Deliver us from evil* sprang to life as vividly as the Neon signs used to flash out around Oxford Circus. For evil *was* real and was imminent.

We were counselled in the newspapers and by all the cheery advisers of the B.B.C. to arrange some place of refuge for use during air-raids.

There was a division of opinion about cellars. The one we possess is excellent – large and airy with two exits and a window, and a small inner room with stone compartments made for wine bottles and very useful to use in the summer for cooling butter.

Our friends advised us to put beds in our cellar, and went so far as to place a candlestick and matches on the top step. Michael had no faith in cellars. When he was in France in the last war he had been buried in one.

Maxwell thought the safest thing to do was to run out into the fields and lie under a hedge. John said a good place for us would be the small square foot or so between the green baize door and the hall. If the house was hit we should have a chance of getting out by back or front doors although, as I reminded him, if the house fell down the doors would probably fall too!

Bunty said she should leap up and lie on her front part under the bed. When they had time she and Mrs. Nonesuch practised the correct attitude, though Mrs. Nonesuch declared that if there really was an air-raid she would be unable to move.

Mrs. Ellison had a real proper dug-out made in her garden. Mr. Martin was its creator. We all went over to see it. It was cemented over and covered with earth. One went down concrete steps to enter the dug-out, which had electric light in the centre and seats round the walls. A tarpaulin covered the entrance, and altogether it was a very neat contrivance.

I came home thinking that on the morrow Michael had better start on a dug-out for us, but John thought our house would stand anything but a direct hit – and anyway he was not going to have me trundling out of doors on a winter's night. A bomb was no worse than pneumonia.

All the same there were few of us at that time who did not put at our bedsides warm clothing, dressing-gown and shoes, just ready to jump into if emergency arose.

Primroses were yellowing every path of the Enchanted Wood, when with consummate strategy and success the enemy took over Denmark and seized the Norselands.

# THE DAYS AHEAD

We dread them! For our Leaders have foretold
    Hard toil with heavy tidings – blood and tears;
    Harvest of our luxurious, careless years,
When for soft-handed ease we lightly sold
The Truth – but would not buy it! Now the cold
    And callous Consequence must chill our ears;
    Now gossips are too glib with gloomy fears
Dreading to see the Scroll of Days unfold.

Courage, my Country! Challenge thy dark hour!
    Shall it be said that hard-pressed England let
    The sun, which rose on her forefathers, set?
This most momentous year may bring the dower
True Britons still must fight for – Peace and Power
    To build for Beauty, and build better yet!


# IF I COULD CHOOSE

If I could choose – then would I wish to be
    Immune from every form of hurt or loss;
    Never to carry grief, nor care, nor cross,
But from disquietude for ever free;
Live out my days and years complacently,
    Keeping my gold from dimness and from dross;
    Holding my treasure tight while others toss
Their riches and their lives away for me?

No! No! I would not choose it – better far
    Lose everything which I have counted sweet;
Better be trampled down as red grapes are
    Than walk unshackled and with unmaimed feet,
Till men and angels say – with lips a'purse:
*There goes the spoilt child of the Universe!*

## Chapter Five

### THE LONG LULL

SPRING CAME TO ENGLAND IN 1940 JUST AS SURELY AS
it came in the years of peace.

We were all very tired of the black-out. The brown
paper at the sides and tops of the windows was showing signs
of wear. The gummed strips on the panes themselves held on
most tenaciously, and it was pleasant to be able sometimes to
open windows top and bottom, and really see the view all at once
instead of seeing it in squares.

But spring was late. We had what our Village calls the
blackthorn winter, for when the wild plum was about to bloom
snow fell again and every budlet shut itself up. Once more
windows could only be opened for brief intervals, draughts swept
under doors and even issued from skirting boards. Once more we
forsook the dining-room, and, as Bunty said, "lived like pigs" in
our only warm apartment.

It was no wonder that this room began to look dirty and
dilapidated. The bright sunshine, untempered by leaves on trees,
with none of the softening effects of summer, showed only too
plainly the state of the furniture. The tapestry which upholstered
settee and easy chairs was wearing thin on the arms and shiny in
the seats, and – in spite of chairbacks – seemed to me to be dirty
along the tops. When we brushed it dust flew out. The curtains

were "tired", the carpet, Mrs. Nonesuch said, needed a good beating on the tennis-court. In short, something dynamic had begun to stir within us, and that something told us, that war or no war, we must without delay begin spring cleaning.

We sent the curtains to the cleaners. We had Mr. Bond, the postman, in to inspect the furniture, for our postman is not only deliverer of letters, he is upholsterer and loose-cover maker to the Village. Mr. Bond, who was gassed in the last war, thought we should soon "be for it" and that those who left their gas-masks at home would deserve all they might get. He advised that a piece of tapestry should be taken from the underseat of the settee to repair the worn places in the chairs, and he agreed to see to that for us.

We turned out and relined cupboards, and we sorted up the contents of chests of drawers; when the upstairs rooms had been dealt with we turned our attention to the kitchen, the pantry and the passage. After long discussion we decided to have the job done properly, although John kept telling me he thought there *was* a war on. Mr. Flower came in. He put clean distemper on the walls and touched up all the doors. Yes, it was a nuisance and we did not like it a bit, but presently things shook into their places.

The drawing-room furniture returned clean and wholesome again. The curtains came back and hung in graceful folds. As we adjusted new chairbacks and clean cushion-covers, we felt that happy feeling which comes when putting finishing touches to work which is well and truly done.

A few – a very few – primroses were showing themselves under the bushes near the front door. They were small, they had no stems to speak of, but set in a bowl of moss they gave the room a springy atmosphere, for we knew they were the promise of good things to come.

In Europe there did not seem to be any good things coming. This waiting, dragging-on game was not getting us anywhere. People began to ask each other what it all meant. John, whom I look upon as a representative man, was frankly worried, and in doubt about the immediate future. Mrs. Nonesuch, who is, I think, also representative of a very large section of the public, asked him almost every day: "Do you think we shall win the war?"

She asked this question wishing to be reassured, and though he teased her a little, John always made the same answer: "Yes, if we pull up our socks!"

Just what he meant I never knew, but it seemed to have a soothing effect upon Mrs. Nonesuch, who lived a good deal of her life in anxiety, as she had brothers in the Army and Navy, and her husband, too, was likely to be called up at any time.

This did not prevent her from working like a Trojan at the spring-cleaning. As we worked she told me her brother's wife and small son, living at a seaport, were spending their nights in a shelter with the roar of guns all over the bay. She told me of her younger brother who had been sent to the Middle East, of her mother whose house was full of young men munition-workers. Through Mrs. Nonesuch many tides washed up to my door. Everyone she knew seemed to be in the war effort. I was the only one whose life ran very largely in the same old channels and who could do little for our fighting men.

Then one day, while we were still in the midst of cleaning, John brought home a young business friend suffering from a breakdown. And John said to me that same evening: "I wonder if we could have Charley Barnard here for a rest?"

So Charley came. He was shy at first. He felt at home with John, but not with Bunty, nor with me. His life had been one long rush, and now that he was ill he did not know how to laze. He did not know how to take a casual and unhurried walk in the country, and he could not bring himself to sit and read. But when the first strangeness had worn off, he seemed content to sit and talk to me during the hours when John could not be at home.

We talked of Charley's wife, of Charley's small son and naturally we talked of Charley. I was knitting a pullover for a deep-sea fisherman and I remember telling him that, although for many years I had lived inland, I had never got used to being without the sea.

He told me about his river – that lovely winding river which runs through Charley's city. He loved it, although he seldom had time to walk beside it. The city which Constable and Hudson made famous, whose cathedral holds up a solemn finger to the sky, bidding men pause in their earthly affairs and give a thought to heavenly things.

John stayed at home one whole day so that we could take Charley for a walk in our woods. We started well wrapped up in winter coats for the wind was cold, but by the time we had climbed to the top of the wood we were so hot it was pleasant to sit on the fallen tree by the mossy path, eat our cakes and look out through the blue haze of morning across the valley towards the Wiltshire hills. World affairs were disturbing. Nature's affairs were going on so gently – almost imperceptibly – yet her slow rhythmic wheel was turning, and would turn, though man might be blind to beauty and deaf to minstrelsy.

A butterfly went by, yellower than the yellowest primrose; a lark sang; almost without interval thrushes lifted up joyous voices; two velvet-brown calves in the Homefield made playful lunges at each other.

Charley, with twinkling eyes, turned to John and said: "If I get much of this I shall not want to go back to business ever again!"

John said: "Ah, you're feeling better!"

Indeed, it was noticeable to all of us that Charley was beginning to get back his strength. He went out in the garden and helped Michael put in the potatoes. Mrs. Nonesuch excelled herself in cooking nice dinners; she reminded Charley to take his medicine, while Bunty's contribution to the good work was a little wholesome teasing. It was pleasant to me to see the serious, set expression disappearing from Charley's face, and when, quite suddenly, he laughed as uncontrollably as a schoolboy, we knew he was on the road to recovery.

Well, Charley went home and subsequently into the Army – and we just managed to get the stair-carpet up and down again before Easter. It seemed to me that this year Easter brought even more than her usual blessedness. The festival fell early, and the flowers were late. Daffodils which usually came to us in mid-March were barely showing a glint of yellow, and on the Saturday after Good Friday only five of those golden ladies had burst their bonds asunder.

To Mrs. Nonesuch and me Saturday must always be an extra busy day. Every room must have a dust-up and a rub-over. There is cooking to be done, and preparation to be made for the morrow.

But this Saturday morning was sunshiny with only a slight tendency to showers. Our valley was putting on her bravery. The waking willows and the larches showed a faint haze of green, and I decided to take those five Lent lilies up to the small gray church on the hill. The cock which sits for ever on the steeple shone like gold, and he had his head turned towards the south-west. Crocuses were showing in the grass which turfed the resting-places of the dead. Inside the church I found the usual band of noble women bent on making her beautiful for Easter Day.

Mine is just a very ordinary housewifely soul, and even then my thoughts had been running a good deal on the fixture bookcases, which this year I was determined should be taken to pieces, so that we could dust the backs of them, and also rescue the teaspoon which had lost itself behind them eighteen months before. But as I entered our old grey church these lesser thoughts dropped away. The flowers on the Communion Table were all of them white and gold. Hyacinths clad in "whiteness most white", and giving forth that intense sweetness which can be heart moving; daffodils, their hoods only half off, decked pulpit and reading desk. Primroses, wind-bitten and small, were set in tiny vases on the window-sills.

Out of the ancient earth, with all its sin and all its sorrow, this loveliness had come. Who could have thought of it? Only the Spirit of the Living Lord could have done this beautiful thing. War would pass, but these would remain, for God is always *true*; His doings are never for the passing moment, but for the eternities.

In our church we have no choir. A few singing men and women sit up in the organ loft, but the real leader of our praise is Mr. Marsh. Sometimes in the middle of a psalm he ceases singing, and immediately there is a "thinning" of the volume – a tailing off – until that rich voice comes in again, when we all do our best to support him.

As we came down the steps from the church on Easter Day, a young man in R.A.F. uniform joined himself to us. It was John's nephew, Edward. He had hitch-hiked from his headquarters, and he came home with us to lunch. That is one of the nice things about relations; you may not meet them very often, nor know them very well, but when they do turn up, then the old saying concerning blood being thicker than water is proved to be very pleasantly true.

Edward slipped into our household straightaway. From that day forward we never knew a day, nor a night, when he might not suddenly turn up. If he arrived after Mrs. Nonesuch had gone, he was quite prepared to get his own supper, and whenever it was possible he helped to lay the table and to clear away. He also helped with the washing-up.

To do this he arrayed himself in one of Bunty's overalls, a brightly coloured, scarlet-poppied affair it was, and Edward, having tied himself firmly at the waist to protect his uniform, stood at the sink and carefully slooshed tumblers, silver, plates, and knives in the most erudite manner possible. He had not been married very long, but his wife had, we told him, brought him up very well.

He replied: "You don't know, Auntie, how jolly it is to be in a home again."

This same period of a century ago has for long been called "the hungry forties", and future historians may surely be justified in describing the present era as "the frightening forties". Hitler was at this time boasting of a secret weapon, and many were the speculations as to its nature. It was hinted in high circles that *we* also had dark and dreadful implements in the making.

It seemed to ordinary folk, like Mrs. Nonesuch and me, that at any moment some terrifying and entirely unthought of crisis might be hurled upon us. Edward brought in a tall story he had heard in camp. It had to do with the discovery by German scientists of an element so powerful that it would annihilate whole populations.

Bunty thought some sort of bacteria might be contemplated. She would, I think, have described in detail the awful symptoms which might result, but Mrs. Nonesuch's horror-stricken face as she brought in the pudding made the narrator desist.

I had an idea myself that, perhaps, we could magnetize the air round the coast of Britain with a current so strong it would draw down invaders into the sea. Water could be magnetized, so why not the air?

"But how would the R.A.F. get back?" asked Bunty.

I replied: "They wouldn't then need to go!"

This was greeted with such roars of laughter that I gave up for ever the idea of inventing a secret weapon.

Not long after this, and while the topic of secret weapons was in everybody's mouth, a very mystifying and unpleasant discovery was made. Miss Cooper, coming home through the water meadows with her dogs, found upon the stile which leads into the wood a red-painted swastika.

At first Miss Cooper could not believe her own eyes – she had passed that way only half an hour before and had seen nothing, and now, just by the leaning ash where the kingfisher so often sits, she saw the hateful and hated symbol of Nazi Germany.

Miss Cooper, having scraped off most of the red paint, dipped her handkerchief in the river mud and rubbed out all trace of the offending sign. She thought some schoolboy had done it for mischief, and was more amused than anything. The next day, however, the red swastika, larger and more defiant than before, again disfigured the humble little stile and again was blotted out by the careful Miss Cooper.

When it appeared a third time she took a walk along the Tyning to the police station and informed Mr. Tring. Mr. Tring is our policeman. Mr. Tring visited the stile, made notes in his notebook, examined the ground for footprints, and frightened the kingfisher away.

The whole thing was, to say the least of it, disturbing, and the Village was properly agitated. Mr. Piggot had seen a man who looked like a spy coming from the station a day or two before. Mrs. Wendover held the opinion that the job had been done by a parachutist. She thought that if careful and exhaustive search were made, a camera and a wireless apparatus might be found.

But nothing further happened. The sunshine became more summery; the wind had fewer rough edges in it. The gardens of the Village were blue with forget-me-nots when we entered upon that most eventful and threatening month – the month of May.

## EASTER EVE

Set high amid green meadow lands,
    With stone and steeple grey,
Our thousand-year-old church serenely stands
    Waiting for Easter Day.

Within, she is made beautiful and young,
    Silver and gold hath she;
Blossoms which from the ancient earth have sprung
    Clothe her most gloriously –
Primrose, and daffodil, and wild white plum –
Waiting with her the Morning that will come.

Here all the unquiet trumpets lull and cease.
Here is the victory! Here is the peace!

## ROGATIONTIDE

In this green and pleasant land,
With its little gardens planned,
Bed and border neatly stored –
Bless us, Lord!
Bless us, Lord!

But in Europe's flowery places,
Desolation fills its spaces,
All the little gardens stricken –
O Lord, quicken!
O Lord, quicken!

Breathe, and with Thy living breath,
Out of dreadfulness and death,
Out of struggle, out of strife –
Bring us Life!
Bring us Life!

## Chapter Six

### THE MONTH OF MAY

IF I WERE ASKED POINT BLANK: "WHEN IS YOUR VILLAGE AT its loveliest?" I should answer: "In the month of May."

Although to me and to many others our Village is beautiful at all times – in mid-winter as well as in summer. Yes, and even in those November days when rain drifts in sheets across our valley; when leaves of brilliant orange and of palest gold are tossed and twirled, and running zig-zag on every lawn; when rain bangs itself down in bucketfuls and all the little gardens look like rag shops – even under such conditions our Village seems a homesome place.

But in the month of May when the primroses are not quite over and the bluebells are beginning – then is the special time when our part of the earth shines like a corner out of Paradise.

I was now able to do much of my knitting and my writing out of doors. Apple trees were in bloom, lilacs and laburnums were at their best, and to all this beauty Nature added one other ingredient which supplied the last ounce of over-weight to the bumping scale of happiness – the nightingales were in full song.

One morning Bunty and I got up at four a.m. to hear the dawn chorus. We stole down the stairs like conspirators, leaving

John asleep in his bed. In the cold dark mist of morning we went through dripping wet fields till we reached the stile leading into Friary Wood. At that moment a nightingale and a blackbird began simultaneously to sing; the two prima donnas of the hedgerow singing together, yet with no emulation and no discord. Quicker than thought the other birds joined them – twos and threes – groups of gleemen – choruses – and presently one grand orchestra fluting, harping, trilling, talking; every bird which had breath was uttering its own note of ecstasy to the harmonious moment.

We saw ghosts of little rabbits running over the white misty fields. But we saw no badgers, though in the mud beside the river Bunty found the undoubted footprint of an otter. The sun rose red and glorious. Cows began to trail their way through wet meadows towards their milking place. We reached home again at seven, stole into the house, and into bed again that none might know of our folly.

A very little later, just as Mrs. Nonesuch ran in, Edward arrived to breakfast, and the eight o'clock news blaring through the house told us that the long dallying was over – Holland and Belgium had been invaded by Germany.

Instantly the air was charged with immensities. This was not the sort of lovely May day when one ate meals and went out and liked being alive. Invasion, for all we knew, was very near. Edward said there was rumour of parachute troops having landed in England.

Bunty dropped out a quick, sharp: "Where?"

Edward nodded mysteriously, but was not to be drawn: "That's a Government secret."

"I don't believe you know."

"Then it's no use expecting me to tell you."

"Were they dressed as nuns?"

Edward munched eggs and bacon, and said sympathetically to John: "Is she always like this?" – who replied: "Only worse!"

The two bread-winners had to run for their train. Edward went out to tinker with his motor bike and met the telegraph boy. All leave was cancelled and he had to return to camp.

I was more sorry than I cared to own. This boy, coming in and out, had added an element which our lives hitherto had rather lacked. Also he was easy to please and liked joining in with all we did. Now he would not be here to taste the first gathered gooseberries on Whit Sunday. We should not hear that horrid motor bike snorting and bursting itself to bits. We should have no one to help us with the washing-up.

Mrs. Nonesuch and I got him off, and after that our usual week-end preparations began. Now I had time to think of Holland – that God-fearing, world-respected nation – suddenly plunged into the devastation of war. Holland who had tried so hard to keep out of it, whose Queen had even sent a message of congratulation to Hitler on his escape from the bomb in the beer cellar. All had been of no avail. In spite of all his assertions that he desired only friendliness and peace, when his planned moment came, the arch-deceiver struck his blow.

As we went around the bedrooms I saw house martins were flying up under the eaves at their old job. They were taking up moistened mud for their nests, and all the while some of them were singing that tiny croodling song which seems to embody in itself the intense ecstasy of homemaking. They did this while guns and bombs were doing their best to shatter all that was peaceable and home-abiding in Europe. Little Belgium over-run for a second time! The scrap-of-paper business enacted all over again! Was honour between nations to perish from the earth? Not while there was a British arm left to strike a blow for truth.

And then – because even when thrones and dynasties are falling someone has to see about meals – I got my basket and went out to do the Whitsun shopping. The Village was decidedly moved. Mr. Merriman stood outside his shop throwing meat to the cats on the wall, but obviously his thoughts were other-where. Yet his air of kindly placidity was undiminished. He threw indulgently, even affectionately, and the cats scrambled and ran and seized their portions, till Mr. Merriman went into his shop again, sharpened his knife and began to serve his customers.

"Half a leg of lamb – No! Madam, but I have half a shoulder. Yes, it is a bad look out for Holland. Two pounds of beef for the dog and no fat, and no skin – well, well, I'm afraid doggy is unfortunate, but I'll see what I can manage."

I met Mrs. Wendover. She is a nice comfortable creature and she dearly loves a gossip, but this morning Mrs. Wendover was put about. She was bound to blame someone, and she blamed

Mr. Chamberlain. She almost stuttered – the words would not come out fast enough. He must have knowed better. What was he thinking of not to have done something? He couldn't help knowing bettern'n we. Why had he let us go into Norway, only to be pitched out again? 'Twas time someone else took over before *they* came and shook the vitals out of us.

That same day the news came through that Mr. Chamberlain had resigned, and Mr. Churchill was appointed Prime Minister.

Someone else had taken over. If, and when, the vitals were shaken out of us we were to know the reason why – and it would not be done without some vigorous inner turmoil being inflicted on the enemy either. Mr. Churchill's portrait which appeared in all the newspapers showed the proper type of Britisher for the job in hand.

*Shurshill* – as our enemies called him – looked the part. His lower lip thrust out, his jaw firmly set, his nostrils wide apart and snuffing up the air like a war horse, he came into what was indisputably "his own". This was his hour – this grim breath-taking, terrifying hour, for which every moment of his life up till now had been a preparation.

Of William Pitt it was said: "He loved England with an intense and personal love. He believed in her power, her glory, her public virtue, till England learnt to believe in herself". This, I cannot help thinking, is the really great and important thing which Mr. Churchill did for England just then.

Our Village, which is I suppose representative of England, was fond of listening to Lord Haw-Haw for the sake of getting a laugh out of his attempts to pulverize the British Empire. This was to us a new type of amusement. At the same time we hated that smug, contemptuous, mocking voice. We knew that it was the voice of a serpent, an emissary of the enemy sent to buffet us. Yet, as we listened to the lying words, in which there was sometimes a thin, a very thin, streak of truth, some hearts began to question within themselves – what if, after all, our leaders knew that Germany was going to win?

On Wednesday of Whitsun-week Holland laid down her arms – and we had thought they were going to let out the water from the dykes in one vast flood, and stop the enemy from advancing. The Queen of Holland, Princess Wilhelmina, and her children had arrived in England, just as England had arrived at what was, perhaps, the most threatening moment in her history.

Queen Wilhelmina spoke on the radio. Her voice was the voice of a woman of great courage and determination, but her position must have been hard in the extreme. My own interest in her began when, as a child, I saw her portrait in a magazine for children. Underneath were the words: The Little Girl Who is a Queen. All through the years – and many have passed since then – Queen Wilhelmina has been known and loved in England. Her way of life, and her way of thinking, seemed to us to have the same steadfast Christian purpose we have seen exemplified in the home-life of our own royal family. She was sad, but she believed that Right would triumph. So did we all – yet, half stunned by this new disaster, something which had been flickering and diminishing in strength for months seemed about to die within us.

And then, just at the crucial moment, with Mr. Churchill at the helm, we took a new grip of ourselves. England who had "so passionately, yet rather indolently" desired peace, knew and accepted the fact that it must be a fight to a finish.

Mr. Churchill's phraseology delighted us. His way of pronouncing the word Nazi with a distinct *r* in it, and as though it were loathsome to his tongue, endeared him to everybody. I think it was just this – that if anyone as high-up as Mr. Churchill could speak like that in the midst of his most solemn speeches, why then, surely, he must know that we were coming through.

Also, he made us feel that we were living in days as momentous as any in our past. When he said: "We have before all of us an ordeal of the most grievous kind", we felt braced and determined to set our teeth and go through with that ordeal whatever it might be.

I well remember that loveliest of Whit-Mondays – with Mrs. Nonesuch out for the day – when everything in the existing order of things seemed about to be shaken, and John had to go to work as usual. Bunty and I went together to Mill Island and lay in the sun close to the weir. Speedwells showed blue in every tussock, and our shoes were yellowed with the gold of buttercups. Little fishes swam just beneath the surface of the water; a dragonfly with green and purple plumes hovered over them. A pigeon flew from an alder – there was a sudden swish, and all the little fishes went head first into the deep of the river.

We came home to find that one of those small, foolishly trying things had happened. The cistern in the bathroom was leaking, and large pools on the floor were slowly seeping through and making a wet patch on the ceiling near the back door. We tried to turn off the water by means of a stop-tap in the larder which is supposed to control all the water in the house. This tap refused to turn.

So before we could have any tea Bunty had to go down to Mr. Flower's house. Naturally, he was not at home, but his wife said he would come up as soon as he returned. We added a few more pans and pails to those already catching drops from the perfidious cistern, and we carried our tea into the garden so that we might not hear the ominous drip-drip which was now getting more insistent.

We had scarcely settled ourselves when, not Mr. Flower, but his deputy, still masticating the remains of his tea, dressed in a brown suit and looking like a good and sensible angel, came in at the round door.

He preceded us up the stairs, and the house was instantly filled with the odours of tobacco and spring onions. Yes, I can remember that, though I cannot so dearly remember what news came through that evening, nor during the following few days. Things seemed just getting worse. Everyone talked of the expected invasion. Everyone said what a pity Belgium had not given up being neutral, and called on us long before; and, also, what good fortune for Belgium that the moment she did call, our men were ready and went at once to her aid.

Just at this point my mother came for a short visit, and the King called the nation to a Day of Prayer. These two things may not seem to be in any way related yet to me, at any rate, they were. Because my mother stands for the old-fashioned, honest-to-goodness and no-nonsense sort of Christian, who had long been convinced that when our nation was on her knees God would be able to bring about His purposes. She said: "This is the most sensible thing we have done since war broke out."

On the Tuesday following my mother and I went to the Roman City to do some shopping. She, I remember, bought at the shop so favoured by Queen Mary a dress length of black *crêpe-de-Chine* dotted with quite lovely little figurings of mauve and blue. Feeling pleased with our purchase we came out into the street to find Mr. Bagshaw waiting beside his car. His face wore an expression of deepest gloom. In his hand he held a copy of a mid-day paper.

Mr. Bagshaw opened the car door – saw us seated – and placed the rug gently over our knees before he put his head in and said: "Belgium's given in!"

It was the lunch hour. As we drove through the city I found myself looking at the faces of the people, deciding which among them was aware of the bad news, and which of them were not.

"King of the Belgians Capitulates Unconditionally!" So said the newspaper, and those persons who knew had a strained and anxious look, and walked as though their thoughts were elsewhere. Those who were still in ignorance looked inconsequent, and just bent on getting home for lunch.

We were late for ours, but Mrs. Nonesuch forgave us when we told her the news. She nearly dropped a vegetable dish: "Oh, how dreadful!" Then she added quickly: "Do you think *France* will give in?"

We assured her that that was impossible. France and Britain would set their teeth and fight like furies – but give in – never!

On the last day of May my mother went home. In the early days of June – that fateful June when we just lived from hour to hour, not knowing what a day or a night might bring forth – Edward turned up. It had been a wild day. At the end of the Nine o'clock News the B.B.C. announced that the Government desired the loan of any number of small boats. We sat together that evening while the wind rose high in the tree-tops and made the windows rattle. There was thunder, there was heavy rain, the newly-formed pears and the apple blossom fell in showers, and we asked each other: "Why did our Government want boats – little boats?" Even Edward and Bunty had no solution to offer. And John, who was full of forebodings, just said: "I don't like it." It was not long before we knew.

The B.E.F. was being withdrawn from France in great jeopardy, but four-fifths of them got safely home. We heard that there was a fierce storm which harassed German bombing planes, but which enabled our troops to pass through to the coast. We heard that the English Channel had never been known to be so calm for so long, so that small craft, pleasure steamers, yachts and motor boats could ply to and fro. The opinion of experts was that possibly 30,000 of our men might be brought to safety. In the end 350,000 reached England.

On the following Sunday there was thanksgiving in all churches for this mercy. On Monday Italy entered the war on the side of Germany, and a desperate onslaught was launched against the French. The enemy did in very truth "come in like a flood". On Thursday he was sixteen miles from Paris and attacking Rheims. On Friday he entered Paris; Monsieur Reynaud made a last desperate appeal to Mr. Roosevelt, and John said he saw nothing to prevent the Germans driving the French Army into the Mediterranean!

I was trying to straighten up the drawing-room – sorting magazines and putting away the week-end muddles, when the news came through that France's army had ceased firing at midnight.

I ran to the kitchen and told Mrs. Nonesuch – she was polishing the dish covers – and we stood looking at each other with awe-struck eyes. She and I had been so much together. We did not profess to understand all the implications and intricacies of this new development, but we could not help knowing that our nation was in grave danger.

Just what this was likely to mean to each one of us, we could only imagine. Mrs. Nonesuch visualized German planes dropping bombs exactly on our glass dome. She seemed to see German storm-troopers rushing in at our front door bent on attacking – me!

The fear which came into my own mind was rather different. I thought the enemy might come along the old Roman road and surround the village while John was at his business in Broadwater, Bunty at her office in Bridgeford, and Mrs. Nonesuch having her afternoon out. Michael, of course, would have rushed off with the Home Guard. We might all so easily be separated for ever, and I should very likely lose my head, and do quite the wrong thing.

Mrs. Nonesuch did not break her mind to me – nor did I break mine to her, but each of us guessed what the other was thinking.

We were remembering our cookings, and our house-cleanings, Bunty's bright additions to our gossipings, John's way of scoffing at our fears, and we were asking ourselves: were all these things to cease, and nothing to be left but fear and horror?

Then Mrs. Nonesuch said: "Well, Hitler's not going to say we didn't have bright covers, anyway!" That I knew was the right line to take, that sort of spirit was going to bring us through, and thus doing small, everyday things we lived through a momentous week. His Majesty's Forces met with disaster after disaster. Mr. Churchill spoke brave words of the honour put upon us; B.B.C. speakers and our newspapers told us of the poor harvests in Europe, of the increasing efficacy of our blockade of the enemy and the growing strength of the Royal Navy.

But we all knew that we were shut up in this little island and were awaiting an expected invasion by sea and by air. We were told to prepare ourselves for bombing; and warned again about carrying our gas-masks. Leaflets issued to every house began thus: "The Germans Threaten to Invade Britain."

It read like a page from the history of England with the green cover, from which my old governess used to instruct her pupils over forty years ago. Only then it was the French who (the big girls said) might land at any moment on the point of the Bristol Channel just opposite our schoolroom.

Now England once more had to be prepared to fight, and to fight desperately, in her own land. Some of us became aware of a terrifying thought lurking always in a secret place at the back of our minds, though never once taken out and looked at – and may God forgive us for having it – the fear that the war was lost.

We began to see great activity in the countryside. Early one morning Mr. Flower was discovered taking down the signpost which had hitherto stood at the cross-roads, pointing the way to the hospital, the Tyning and the old Roman road which runs westward. The Village treated this as a great joke. Women hurrying to work stopped to ask Mr. Flower the way to their "places". The butcher's boy and the baker's boy stood affecting bewilderment. Mr. Bagshaw halted his car, Mr. Nonesuch braked his van, and to all of them Mr. Flower gave the same advice – if they followed their noses they would get somewhere, anyhow.

Our solitary milestone – Four miles to the Roman City – was tipped upside down over the hedge into a field. The name of our Village disappeared from the railway station overnight. And our own county's special landmark – the Whitehorse on the Westbury Hills – was blotted out. This was a more grievous and more personal matter, for how were we to know what weather we were going to have, now there was no weather forecast and we could no longer see the White Horse?

When mist is driving over the 'orse everybody knows we are in for a wet spell. When the sun directly upon it, showers are likely; but when the White Horse is a silver shield shining through a blue haze, then we look for settled weather.

In the green fields which border the main road a steam excavator was at work digging a mighty trench which, it was said, was part of a scheme of fortifications to protect our nearest seaport.

In Abbey Lane, that peaceable and lovely little stretch of road, we had a glimpse of the searchlight unit. The lads belonging to that had the reputation of being always hungry. In the strong, pure air which blows from the Wiltshire Downs, appetites were terribly sharpened, and when transport wagons were late bringing their breakfasts the hefty lads went to Mrs. Perkins at the farm, who fed them loaves of home-baked bread straight from her oven.

It was no unusual thing for Mr. Nonesuch, out with the bread van, to be halted by young soldiers of the King and obliged to let them have all the nice crusty loaves they desired.

Down by the river we discovered workmen putting up a small brick building. We went forward thinking to have a word with them, but we found they were all strangers – neither Perce nor Harry, nor even Artie was among them.

One of the delights of living in a village is that you know the real villagers by their Christian names. In the Village everyone talks to everybody else, and it seems to us churlish and unfriendly not to pass the time of day, even with strangers. But these workmen looked at us suspiciously. Nearby stood a charabanc, which plainly said they had been brought from a distance. Our "Good afternoon!" elicited a distinctly unfriendly grunt, and we passed on without further parley. Nearer the weir another "house" was in course of erection.

Soon we knew that they were block-houses, and very cleverly were they camouflaged to look like old sheds, hayricks, or small cottages. When they were finished, and the unfriendly workmen had departed in their charabanc to build others elsewhere, the Village visited them and had many comments to make. Mrs. Wendover, being so comfortably proportioned, could only with great difficulty get in – but she did get in, and pronounced the peep-holes far too small.

Other "defences" were concrete foundations for iron barricades which were in course of construction across both ends of the bridge by the mill.

Heaps of stones and huge blocks of granite were placed at intervals in our widest fields to prevent the safe landing of German planes and troop carrying gliders.

How very often, as one mode of defence followed another, I was reminded of the old history of England, portions of which I had in my young days to learn by heart.

"The Norman castles," thus ran one of the paragraphs, "were built for safety, not for comfort." Then followed a detailed description of the measures taken. The teeth of the portcullis – of which there was a picture – were amazingly like the toothed, iron things which stood propped up against hedges and fences at almost every corner of our steeply winding roads, in readiness for insertion into their concrete sockets to form a barricade should the need arise.

The peep-holes left in the walls of the block-houses were just the same as those left in castle towers, and through which arrows were shot at any approaching foe. That this sort of thing should again be necessary in our England seemed too strange to be true.

# THE MAN OF THE HOUR

When the hour had struck and the World's round eyes
    Were questioning Britain's power,
Swift as the shaft of an arrow flies
    Up rose the man of the hour.

"Come men! Come men! Will you travel with me
    On a road where the war flames glower?
I have but one aim! It is victory!
    Come men!" cried the man of the hour.

"I have nothing to offer, and nothing to get,
    Neither glory nor golden dower;
Only toil and tears, and blood and sweat
    Will be yours," said the man of the hour.

Then up flamed the fire of the British race,
    And the men who were Britain's flower
Left hearth and home, and the market-place
    To follow the man of the hour.

## THESE ARE GREAT DAYS

These are great days for living in –
    The greatest ever known!
Now all he has and all he is
    No man can call his own.

Though Peace and Joy and Loveliness
    Are driven from the earth,
And Place and Power and Property
    Are less than nothing worth,

Yet Valour walks our way again –
    Walks with her head held high!
Service and Sacrifice keep house
    And Selfishness must die!

*Chapter Seven*

## UNDER THE SHADOW OF INVASION

THE MIDSUMMER SILENCE HAD SETTLED DOWN UPON our woods and meadows. Birds and beasts were reaching a period when ecstatic and precarious living had given place to a more sober enjoyment of peace and plenty. The first families of the year were now able to look after themselves. Seeds, caterpillars, aphis, and all kinds of herbage flourished in abundance. Young finches – gold – green – and the ubiquitous chaffy played at Touch around and in the bird baths.

Minute apples and pears showed themselves amid abundant foliage, and everything which could bear fruit gave signs of being abundantly fruitful. This, Michael said, was because the buds had made no false starts, and therefore had experienced no setbacks. The intense cold had kept everything in check until the proper time for flowering arrived.

The gooseberry bushes were loaded – even the bullfinches we had seen on them had apparently been unable to get rid of all the buds. Our tall, white lilies were in bloom once more, and Bunty and I were picking raspberries after tea when one of Mr. Hazeldean's young people came straying towards us with a telegram. This was from Mr. and Mrs. Sands. It stated that they were motoring from the South-East coast, and hoped to reach us some time before midnight.

I have noticed for a long while now that, whenever visitors arrive with any degree of unexpectedness, it always happens to be the helper's afternoon and evening out. Mrs. Nonesuch says she has got quite used to finding a note on the kitchen table, the morning after her off-time, to say that Mrs. or Miss So-and-So is in the spare-room and would like breakfast in bed.

In this case, however, the arrival was not entirely unexpected. We had weeks before told the Sands to come to us, at any hour of the day or night, should it ever become necessary for them to leave their home. Therefore the spare bed was made up, the room in order, and we had only to put the last-minute touches, while John went round to the farm for a quart of milk.

As we pottered around preparing a meal I was telling Bunty some of my memories of the old days, when Mrs. Sands and I used to go out together, each pushing a pram containing our respective babies. Tommy Sands, very plump and contented, grasped a woolly rabbit; Bunty Inchfawn had a white cat speedily becoming grey, because it was thrown out of the pram so often. Tommy Sands never sucked the spotless ribbons of his spotlessly white hat. Bunty Inchfawn's bonnet strings were chewed to pulp. Tommy's pram cover remained tidily tucked in, and Tommy's fat hands lay placidly upon it. Bunty's cover was creased and crooked, because she was always kicking and pulling it. She frequently threw it into the road just for the fun of seeing her mother pick it up again.

Mr. Sands was rather younger than John. They had worked together on a newspaper for years, and when we took up our tent pegs and decided to return to the Westland the parting caused real regret to each of us.

The Sands arrived that summer evening between nine and ten o'clock. They had been motoring for over twelve hours. What they could bring of their worldly goods had been packed into the car with them. Much of the small township in which they lived was being evacuated for occupation by the military. They had left their business premises, their home and their furniture, not knowing whether they would see any of these things again.

There was much to hear and much to talk over. We all seemed able to pick up the threads of our friendship exactly where we left off, without any long ravels of explanation. Things were just the same, only that now we had Bunty – tall, alert, and very much alive, listening to us with interested attention, able to make tea and to fill Mrs. Sands' rubber bottle – instead of a small, fat child who had to have honey put into her mouth to keep her quiet for five minutes.

Mr. Sands was as cheery and as humorous as he was in our early days of house-keeping, yet his business had gone, and the town in which it was situated was in a parlous state. People who had friends with whom they could stay were having their fares paid for them to go away.

We lingered a long time over supper. Then Bunty and Mrs. Sands went out to call our cat, and we learned that Timmy Sands had been put to sleep the day before because his owners had no settled home, and could not leave him behind. Cat-lovers all the world over will know something of what that meant.

Tigger, our red tabby Tigger, died suddenly during the cold winter, and we now had a kitten – brindled and long-haired – whose name was Haddy. Haddy's past was rather spectacular. He was discovered with his two brothers, all tiny, half-wild creatures, wandering in our garden in winter weather.

They were starving, yet too timid to let us approach them. They were seen chewing ravenously at scraps of bread which the birds dropped under the high wall of the yard. Bunty spent much of her spare time carrying bread and milk round the garden, and depositing it near the wood pile where she hoped the kittens would find it. Michael made a little house out of a tea box. It was like a chicken's pen with a draw-up door. This he filled with hay and placed with its back to the wind, and its entrance to the wood pile.

The three kittens took possession of the house immediately. They began to know the tinkling sound Bunty made with the plate of food. It was not long before they came to meet her, and finally they all followed her into the kitchen and decided to be house-cats.

The next morning Mrs. Nonesuch took Mrs. Sands her breakfast in bed, and while she was putting the tray down it was discovered that Mrs. Nonesuch's brother and Mrs. Sands' second son Lionel, who was in the Fleet Air Arm, had been together on the same aircraft-carrier.

This was indeed a bond! Now we were to get inside information concerning some of the things we had only read of in the newspapers. Mrs. Sands is not one of those tiresome people who only tell you the barest details of the most stirring affairs; in relating a story she begins at the beginning and goes on to the end, telling the small, interesting, in-between incidents which every woman likes to know.

We soon realized that we were only outsiders and that Mrs. Sands was an initiate. She had had to have the windows of her home boarded up, to turn the key in the door, and leave her furniture to run the risk of bombardment from sea and air. She had watched "dog fights" over the coast. She had heard, and had felt, the thunder of the guns, and seen the red flares in France.

She had seen many of the little boats set out and return loaded from Dunkirk. She knew many of the men, and some who were only lads in their teens, who had sailed their tiny boats and brought back their precious cargoes. She had lived, literally, not knowing what a day or a night might bring forth, and as we looked at her, so tired and heavy-eyed – glad just to sit alone upon the green bank letting, so she said, "the peace of Innisfree soak in" – we felt how far removed our own lives had been from the death and danger which was in the world, how little, up to the present, we really knew of the nearness and the ruthlessness of the enemy.

We were soon to know a little more. German planes were overhead every night, sirens were continually wailing. Loud thuds punctuated what had once been the silent hours. They were near enough to rattle our windows. Of course John, Bunty and Mr. Sands rushed outside. From the shelter of the porch Mrs. Sands and I could see a red glare in the sky, looming between the tall fir trees which face our front door. I knew very well that this meant an attack was being made upon our City of the West, and my mother and my sister Griselda were living there.

The thuds continued. The night was clear and starlit, and a network of searchlights – long feeling fingers – moved slowly up the sky, crossing and re-crossing each other. Shells from anti-aircraft guns were bursting continually.

We heard men running in the road below. A dog on the opposite hillside was barking, and all the dogs within hearing were lifting up their voices, too. Eventually we went to bed, but there was little sleep for anyone that night.

Bunty phoned to her grandmother early next morning. She was cheerful and quite calm. Yes, the city had been bombed; they had been in the cellar most of the night and Griselda had made tea down there on a spirit stove. But they were not leaving home at present – though if things got worse they would consider coming to us. She hoped we should not worry about them. My mother was quite decided, and for the time being things remained as they were.

One morning my helper and I were busy with the bedrooms when Mrs. Sands came to us with horror written in capital letters upon her face.

"Listen!"

Through the open window we heard a metallic *dong – dong – dong – dong –*

"The church bell!" said Mrs. Sands. "That means invasion!"

So it had come! Come most probably as John had always said it would – by parachute on the Downs. The Germans would pour along our Wiltshire roads, past the White Horse – or what had been the White Horse – through the old town with the gables and over Woodwick Hill.

All this went through my mind in the space of a second.

"They will probably use gas," said Mrs. Sands.

"And I've left my gas-mask at home!" Mrs. Nonesuch's eyes dilated.

My thoughts flew to my two bread-winners – gone, I knew, without the protection which Mr. Bond said everyone ought always to carry with them.

*Dong – dong – dong –* then the sound suddenly ceased.

I looked at the clock. The hands stood at ten precisely.

"Oh, it was only the church clock!"

Mrs. Nonesuch's relief was unmistakable. We all three gave a rather tremulous snigger, and Mrs. Sands said we ought, anyway, to be prepared, but she was sorry to have frightened us.

Our ordinary life went on. Often, as we sat in the window seat in the wide bay overlooking the lawn, and Mrs. Nonesuch brought in the tea wagon with its plates full of scones and home-made cakes, we said to each other: "This is not a wartime tea!"

And to Bunty's amusement I could not help recalling the food difficulties of the last war.

How to get enough to eat really was a daily problem then. Rationing did not begin till 1917, and frequently we could get no butter, and no sugar, and no meat – therefore no dripping! The queues were long, and those who could push hardest got the goods. The bread, I recollect, at one time was yellowish and dry, with bits in it which looked like chaff. The margarine was streaky and rancid.

But even in that war Mrs. Sands' experiences were grimmer than mine. Her husband was in France. The night her second son was born a Zeppelin dropped bombs over the town. It was attacked by our planes and brought down, and as Lionel had come into the world to the accompaniment of the roar of aircraft, it seemed only right that he should now be in the Air Force.

July came in – July with her warm nights, her glow-worms, and her long lovely days, when we could sit in the garden from dawn till dark, working and talking and sometimes doing nothing, but just being thankful, I hope, for the peace and rest of our environment.

Even during this direful summer we had happy and almost carefree times yet, without trying to improve the occasion, I can honestly say that the thoughts which came to us then – when we all fell silent, when we were quite alone – were different thoughts from those which on ordinary days float around the surface of the mind. Somehow we lived deeper, as folk do who are on the fringe of great events.

The threat of invasion was about us every hour of every day. Mr. Nonesuch heard many strange things when on his rounds. He was informed on good authority that the date of the attack was fixed for the ninth or the nineteenth, his informant was not quite sure which. He also heard that the King was busy packing up his crown and was going to an unknown destination because, by August, the Swastika would be flying over Buckingham Palace and Hitler would be eating his dinner there.

It has always been the English way to laugh at the pomposity of enemy claims, therefore we laughed, and everybody else laughed, at the preposterous idea. But it was just then, more than at any other time, that I really and truly "saw fear".

Looking back on those days I think that I was probably very tired. The Sands had now left us. It had been decided that Mr. Sands should manage the business Charley Barnard had to leave when he put on the King's uniform. With the departure of our visitors some of the zest and the exhilaration of living in such great days seemed to evaporate. We had had no holiday; it was useless to think of one. John's hands were quite full from before nine in the morning till after seven at night, and even if that had not been the case – there was nowhere to go! The coast was out of the question, and something seemed to warn me not to go far away from home lest I found myself unable to return.

Home and country had become inexpressibly dear during this time of world upheaval. One did not need to be told

> Look thy last on all things lovely
> Every hour.

Most of us were only too conscious of the fact that we might at any time be looking our last upon the old well-known ways of life. By and by, when the history of those days is written down for an interested world to read, many small and unimportant details will be noted and seized upon. People will like to know what we had to eat, and how we passed our days; and some there will be who would like to ask us this question: "Did you find that you possessed anything of a spiritual nature strong enough to uphold you just then?"

The answer to that question is: We did!

This force, this upholdment, this energizing and strengthening power or whatever you like to call it, came, not in long lengths, but in little lengths, just enough to carry us over the day's need.

Speaking for myself, I never once felt that I had any accumulation of calmness or of steadfastness; my upholdments came to me chiefly in small and ordinary happenings. Mrs. Ellison would come in and bring her knitting, and we sat together, she with her khaki socks and I with my Air Force pullover; Edward would arrive bringing with him the merry fearless atmosphere of youth.

Edward was a radio-operator, and when the "chappies" were learning to fly he had to keep in touch with them by radio.

I asked him: "What do you say?"

"Oh, anything, Auntie. It is nearly all question and answer. The great thing is to keep in touch with them every second. I say: 'Are you airborne?' and he replies: 'I am airborne.' And after that it is almost any old thing. I even read to them from the poets – it doesn't matter what – so that they answer, and we know where they are. Just anything to keep communication going."

Perhaps one of the greatest helps came to me from the daily noontide prayer services at the old grey church. As often as I could I planned my work so that I could slip away just at ten minutes to twelve, and join the band of worshippers there. It was not a large band. That was not possible on a week day and at a time when most persons were working at full pressure. Those who went with any sort of regularity could be counted on one's fingers.

A certain lady in a bonnet and veil, known in the Village as "The Deaconess", was always present. So was her sister Edith, who nearly always brought Mrs. Simmons who is blind. There was also Mrs. Allen, sprightly and dark-haired; Miss Ross, who looked a trifle prim until she smiled; Mrs. Sowerby, who hailed from Yorkshire, and Miss Gillian, with peace in her eyes and on her forehead. These with a few others seemed to be the praying people. It was to me a tremendous privilege to meet with them, and sometimes to have a brief moment with one or another outside the church. Bunty and John alluded to them as "Mother's little friends", but even they could not know how welcome to me was the lift and the comradeship of that prayer service.

Dean Barrett led our prayers. A very tall old man was the Dean, he was retired now and lived in our Village. He was deaf, and he spent much of his spare time wandering over our woods and hilly fields looking for rare wild flowers. The Dean's prayers were very often extempore, and I place them among the truly beautiful things which came my way just then.

"Arm us, O God, with the weapons of the Overcomer."

"We would not pray to be always safe in this world – but always in Thy keeping."

"Let not the despairing nations lose the will to be free."

"Though our enemies come in like a flood, Thy will is the encirclement beyond which they cannot pass."

Fay Inchfawn.

INNISFREE: *Aerial view showing the house in its grounds with Glenthorne at top left. Below, a photo showing the east elevation.*

BRITANNIA AT IFORD: *'River! Why does Britannia stand
On your gray bridgehead far inland ?'*

WARD'S LIBRARY: *'A high gabled building set in surely the most awkward of corners.'* This photo was taken in 2008 during restoration.

THE HERMITAGE: *'Standing high upon the hillside, its foundations set quite literally upon rock, The Chantry has a beauty which is clear-cut and austere.'*

LIMPLEY STOKE HOTEL: *'Our beautiful Hydro passed into the possession of a business firm known as the Belfry Road Building Society.'*

PILLBOX: *'Soon we knew that they were block-houses, and very cleverly were they camouflaged to look like old sheds, hayricks or small cottages.'*

LIMPLEY STOKE CHURCH: *'I decided to take those five Lent lilies up to the small gray church on the hill. The cock which sits for ever on the steeple shone like gold, and he had his head turned towards the south-west.'*

AROONA: *'I ran in at the gateway of Mavoureen, halted, and decided that Mrs. Frobisher might think I was mad.'*

THE INN: *'Still, the Village took its walking sticks and went down the steep hill to the old hostelry, where the London coaches used to swing around the bending road with a flourish and a trumpeting of the posting horn.'*

EVACUEES: *Bombed-out residents of Bath, typical of the evacuees who turned up in Freshford in the days following the Baedeker Raids of April 1942.*

THE SCHOOL: *'In the afternoon the victims of the raid began to come in. Two elderly women were the first to arrive. They had walked the whole way – five miles – and were dead beat.'*

WESLEYAN CHAPEL: *'In this small Bethel the mothers found sanctuary. One girl had walked in the lanes for two nights carrying her few-weeks-old baby. But all she said was: "Oh! isn't it nice to sit down?"'*

## UNDER THE SHADOW OF INVASION

These were some of the phrases which Dean Barrett put into his players; though the bare printed words give no idea of their intensity, of their earnestness, nor of the vast expanse of universe which seemed to open before the eyes of the soul as this trustful spirit poured itself out before God.

And every day he named with a pause after each, the names of the young men of the Village who were serving in His Majesty's Forces. He always added these words: *Shelter them in the day of battle, and enable them in life, or in death, to put their trust under the shadow of Thy wings.*

## ENGLAND, I HAVE NEVER TOLD YOU

England! I have never told you
How exceeding dear I hold you!
All my nights and all my days
I have known your generous ways;
From your loom – of your bright weaving
Came my hope and my believing;
Ere my wonder could awaken
You had given – I had taken –
Language, liberty and beauty,
Honour, truth and sense of duty
I – to liquidate such giving –
Can but offer all my living,
Yielding up the liberty
Which so long you gave to me.
Though you lead through fire and water –
England – England! let me be
Worthy to be called your daughter!

## WHEN ENGLAND FALLS

When England falls let me lie still
Beside her on an English hill.
When England sinks then may I be
Drowned with her in an English sea.
If England must be crucified,
Broken and bleeding, and cast aside –
Oh, then, beneath an English sky
With England – *England* – let me die!

*Chapter Eight*

## THE SOUND OF THE SIREN

THE SOFT FRUITS WERE ALL GATHERED, THE HOUSE had received the special clean-down which is always necessary after visitors. A certain tang in the morning air told us that summer had passed high-water mark. Short-sleeved dresses had to be supplemented with a cardigan, and those who possessed thin and chilly arms were even glad to put on a coat. When you take to a coat for garden wear, then the time is fast approaching when that garment must be replaced.

Bunty and I had decided to go to the Roman City and take a look round the shops. The train was, of course, very late, but that gave us time to sit on the station seat and with Mr. Winch, the porter-in-charge – for our station is not large enough to boast a station-master all on its own.

We admired the station garden which is very properly the pride of Mr. Winch's heart. He has looked after it for over thirty years. Passengers lean out of carriage windows to exclaim about it. Our station garden, I should think, is well known to everybody within a radius of fifty miles. In fact I heard about it once in the North of Scotland!

That afternoon the garden flamed with nasturtiums, dahlias and gladiolus, with ageratum and white alyssum for an edging. Yellows and scarlets formed the chief colour scheme, but purples and mauves crept into it.

The whole Village takes a real interest in the station garden; choice roots and choice seedlings from the big houses find their way into it, but Mr. Winch is himself its devoted servant and creator. He pointed out to us a crimson rose with some late blooms on it. Mr. Winch's daughter had a slip of it given her by the ladies at whose house she worked.

This led us to ask about Jessica's young man, Albert, who was in the army and stationed in Yorkshire. And that led us to the war, and Mr. Winch's opinion was that we should have to take some hard knocks yet.

The noontide sun shone full upon the garden. White jessamine was twining itself over the low wall beside the booking office. The scent of it had reached an unknown traveller, who had written to Mr. Winch to thank him for it. The letter was just addressed: The Station Master of the Glorious Garden, Near Roman City, and there being no other such garden anywhere near, the epistle came quite safely to Mr. Winch.

"I tell you I was pleased – very pleased, indeed, I was," and Mr. Winch's cheerful face became more beaming than before. "I put in hours at the garden – I've a love for it, you see – and I know it pleases people when we get First Prize in the Company's Gardens Competition. But it isn't often a stranger will take the trouble to sit down and write a letter about it. But this gentleman did. The jessamine reminded him he said of his old mother's garden. He's travelled all about the world, and not seen a garden that made him think of that – not the same way as ours did." At this point the train was signalled, and Mr. Winch retired to the booking office and began to issue tickets.

We sped upon our way to the Roman City, we went up the wide historic street beloved of Beau Nash, and in *Cheerables'* window, which is Queen Mary's special shop, Bunty saw a hat which she said looked just like me.

It was a shady hat of speckled gray straw, with a neat and good look about it, which pleased me mightily – as Pepys would say. To go with it we found a gray tweedy costume with military pockets, but yet not too dashing for a woman who is "getting on" to wear. A scarf with royal blue in it added the necessary touch of colour, and I felt myself set up for a long time to come. The parcel was packed up, and we decided to catch the first bus home as the trains were so uncertain. We were on our way to the door when the siren sounded.

Instantly the outer doors were fastened, and we with the other customers were conducted to *Cheerables'* basement. Here on a platform, we found long upholstered backless benches arranged in rows, as if for a meeting. The upholstery was in delicate flowered damask. On these benches we all sat; they were old benches and seemed quite in keeping with the atmosphere of *Cheerables*. I should not be surprised to learn that they had once been used to accommodate dowagers and chaperones around the walls of the Assembly Rooms. It was rather a come-down for them to be used just for customers to sit on during an air-raid. Though of course, but for itinerant exceptions like ourselves, *Cheerables'* clientele, being the last word in gentility, sat in a dignified and aristocratic way with their fashionable hats suitably tilted; grasping their matching hand-bags in beautifully gloved hands.

Behind us we could not help hearing snatches of conversation: "It happened just at midnight – the Colonel said: 'Good heavens! They've got the Abbey'."

"We make the gardener and the maids practice what to do in the case of an incendiary. Dobbs throws down a tin of Vim and Cook smothers it with sand."

"You get a jelly square and melt half of it with hot milk."

"We all squeezed into the cupboard with the gas meter, and Ernest sat on Aunt Ruth's Persian cat. My dear! The fuss there was."

Bunty and I were in the front row, and she got out her sea-boot stockings, and I got out my navy mittens. It was now four o'clock, just when we should have been walking up the hill from the bus with the prospect of tea before us, and a chance to gloat over our purchases.

For one hour and fifty minutes we sat in that basement knitting and longing for tea. The staff trooped past us going for theirs! We saw several familiar faces – the young ladies from the glove counter, the presiding genius of the hat department, and the queenly "head" of the coats and costumes.

Trays full of teapots passed tantalizingly before our eyes. There was a pleasant chink of cups. Huge plates of bread and butter and cake were carried by. Furniture men with aprons appeared from the back premises, and hovered round. The young man who had once come out to advise us about a new carpet stood against the wall holding a tin hat.

The customers were all getting very tired of it, and we were considering making a dash for the train, or for the bus (whichever we could catch first) when joyfully, and very suddenly, the All Clear went!

Up the stone stairs we hurried to the ground floor, every one of us, including the most distant and dignified, all smiling broadly with relief as we were let out. That street! It was like the street of Hamlin City when the townsfolk poured into it to see the children following the Pied Piper.

Such hurry! Such laughter! Such gesticulation! People bumped against each other, pointing upwards to indicate in which direction the German planes had gone, followed by our Spitfires. Cars hooted trying to negotiate a way through the stream of humanity suddenly loosed. Everyone was talking, everyone seemed merry, and the feeling of release was uppermost as, by the skin of our teeth, we caught a departing bus and rumbled towards home.

We had our belated tea and were just washing up the cups when Mrs. Nonesuch returned, very much worried about us, for she had heard that an enemy plane had dropped bombs, and had later been brought down within a mile of the Roman City.

When she discovered that we had had no tea offered to us her indignation was great! She kept saying: "I would not have believed it of *Cheerables*. I thought theirs was the politest, grandest shop in these parts. No tea! I shan't think anything of them again!"

Bunty laughed at Mrs. Nonesuch, telling her that *Cheerables* would have to engage an extensive staff of cooks and washers-up if they undertook to provide free teas for all those who were glad to take shelter with them during air-raids.

"Did you see the German planes, Miss?" said Mrs. Nonesuch. "Mrs. Wendover says that *she* did. She says she saw high up in the sky a lot of things as small as insects darting in and out of the clouds as if they were playing Touch. But she always sees more than anybody else!"

I am afraid we thought, with Mrs. Nonesuch, that this was just one of Mrs. Wendover's tall stories, until a few days later

Mrs. Ellison told us that she and Jane had distinctly seen an air battle going on. The shift and play of the planes above, and round about the clouds, was like some Lilliputian combat. It was real and awful all the same, though so far above the earth that no noise of engines – only the faint vibration of guns could reach human ears.

How few of us were aware that these were the beginnings of the Battle of Britain! Germany was seeking a decision which would end the war in her favour. While the devoted "few" were fighting for our lives, we were among the "many" who were occupying themselves with the small difficulties of the passing days.

The date when Hitler was to fly the Crooked Cross over Buckingham Palace came and went without this consummation, and Mrs. Nonesuch seemed rather more comfortable in her mind.

Edward, whose visits had become very frequent, now put before us a suggestion that he should make our house his headquarters. All the chappies had been told to sleep away from camp if they could. German planes were over bombing every night and the chappies were getting so little rest something of this sort was becoming imperative.

"We get planes over here, you know, Edward," said Bunty.

"Yes, Bunty, but they're out looking for us." And he added thoughtfully: "If I come you will get my extra sugar ration."

I said solemnly: "Edward, will you promise not to start up that snorting dragon of yours just under my window in the early morning?"

"There shan't be one snort *ever*, Auntie."

"Not a smell?"

"Not the ghost of a smell."

So Edward came. He arrived each evening in time for late tea. And he left just after seven in the morning after a hurried breakfast put ready for him overnight.

September's golden days were far advanced and I was busy putting finishing touches to a nature story. The morning went so quickly I had not realized that it wanted only a quarter to twelve. As I ran upstairs for my shoes the siren went, but in the country we took little notice of sirens and within a minute or so I was hurrying along the garden path, taking a short cut over the tennis-court on my way to church.

As I went out of the round door in the wall I heard what seemed to me queer noises overhead – noises like very loud motor engines punctuated by explosions. Over the top of our lime trees two planes were passing. I did not *like* the lowness of them, nor the ear-deafening noise they made. Our neighbour Mrs. Wick was busy hanging out her washing. She spoke to me, and I spoke to her, but neither of us could hear what the other said, and I went on up the hill as quickly as I could.

This hillside road is steep and as a rule very quiet, except when army lorries rush up and down – but now those explosive noises made the very air vibrate, and suddenly I experienced fear. What if the planes should be dive-bombers? Would they machine-gun a solitary woman walking on a country road? I wondered whether I had better throw myself down flat on the footway against the high wall, or under the hedge on the other side where there was no pavement and where a lorry might easily rumble over me before I had a chance to get up.

I ran in at the gateway of *Mavoureen*, halted, and decided that Mrs. Frobisher might think I was mad. I ran out again determined to take shelter in the church, when I saw Mrs. Frobisher's gardener and young Harry Frobisher standing on the top of the high wall looking through field-glasses.

I said: "What is it?"

Harry said: "An air battle! They have just brought down a German plane in the fields beyond Friary."

My heart slowed up a little and I went on. The little service had begun. My legs and hands were shaky, and I was glad to kneel and get back some of the breath which seemed to have forsaken me.

On returning home I found my helper very white and scared-looking. She had watched the planes from the shelter of the stairs through the back door. She had heard "things" falling on the roof and in the nut bushes. Afterwards she and Bunty picked up pieces of metal and empty cartridge cases. There was scarcely a garden or a house in the village which had not been peppered with these mementoes from the sky.

It seems that the German planes had made a surprise attack upon an aircraft works. On their return they had passed directly over Broadwater and John said they looked exactly like brown trout nosing their way up-stream. Our Spitfires were continually attacking them, and they had destroyed six before they could reach the coast.

But our own losses were grievous. Men and women of the district who had left their homes well and hearty in the morning were lying dead beneath masses of fallen masonry. Mrs. Wendover's son-in-law was among them. This brought the terrible tragedy home to us, and during the next few days we learned rather more of what it means to be at war.

Peace had gone from us, so it seemed – suddenly and imperceptibly. We had not realized how happy we had been until we had lost the precious thing which had made our blessedness. We were none of us free – as we had once known freedom. We were all of us restricted in one way or another – but this was a trivial matter compared with the new realization of the uncertainty of life.

London, now a battle-field, was going through her ordeal by fire. Homes, particularly working-class homes, were ablaze. Londoners have always loved the excitement of a fire. The sight of the fire-engine manned by her gallant company in shining helmets has been sufficient to send thousands running to the scene of action.

Now the need was not pivotal but wide-spread, and the London firemen, fire brigades and auxiliaries were fighting with the courage of Englishmen.

To us, who were not Londoners, it came as a shock to hear that the well-known places dearly loved by English folk had been special targets for our enemies. St. Paul's, the Guildhall, Buckingham Palace, Tower of London – in our youth we had come up from the country specially to visit and to stare at them. Then they appeared to be solid enough to last for all time. Now shattered windows, piles of wreckage and huge craters showed the pitiless nature of the foe with whom we had to deal.

And now to our Village came a steady stream of strangers from danger areas. We still had none sent to us, but Bunty was by this time putting in certain hours each week at the Cottage Hospital. She went off in her white apron with the Red Cross upon it, carrying her cap in her hand, and my part was still to help to keep the house going and do odd jobs when I could. One evening as I was prowling in the kitchen I heard Mrs. Nonesuch hurrying through the back entry.

"Oh! Madam, I've got two evacuees."

She stood there, dark-haired, clear-skinned, with that intense look of living to the full which makes her such good company at all times, and it seemed to me that Mrs. Nonesuch having evacuees was next-door to having them myself. While she scrubbed the potatoes she told me all about this new adventure.

Mrs. Wills had come in her car and had brought an elderly couple. A tall, fresh-coloured man, and a short, stoutish woman who wore ear-rings and was of the old Dutch type. As she gave them their tea, the wife told Mrs. Nonesuch some of their experiences.

"It was only last night, dear, and Dad and me went to the shelter where we all of us have to go every night now. When we came out this morning and went up our street our block of flats was gone. Down on the ground, dear! Every stick of it – nothing left but a heap of rubbish."

Mrs. Nonesuch, deeply sympathetic, asked whether they had lost everything.

"Yes, dear! I had made a batch of lovely cakes too, and left them on the kitchen table. There was £2 in my handbag on the dresser. I had slipped my best ear-rings into the teapot, which I often do for convenience, a lovely pair they were. And my teeth I had left on the shelf by the sink. Uppers and lowers, dear! That's why I can't talk plain. And my clothes, and Dad's clothes – they've all gone. We've only got what we have on."

"There – there, Missus – the lidy don't want to know all about us" – the old man kept his hand on the old woman – to cheer her up he said, for she was on the verge of tears.

"And while we were standing there looking, and the neighbours all round staring, wondering whether we could find any of our things, and the policeman keeping us off, who should come up, quite sudden and unexpected in a car, but our King and Queen.

"And he got out, and she got out, and they talked to us so pleasant and friendly, and said how sorry they were for us. Now, I ask you, wasn't it kind of that Lady, and that Gentleman, with all they must have to do in a day, to come down our way and tell us that?"

"I wish," said Mrs. Nonesuch to me, "that I could tell it like they did. First she would tell a bit, and then the old man would correct her, and then he would go on and tell a bit more. When I showed her the bedroom they're to have, the poor old thing began to cry and said: 'God will make it up to you. I never thought I should ever be without a home.'"

## THAT DREADED HOUR

If it should come to me – that dreaded hour –
    Death and destruction raining from the sky,
    With no safe hiding-place, nor refuge nigh,
How should I meet it? Should I shrink and cower
Clinging to others – stripping them of power
    To succour those more needy? Oh! should I
    Be a fear-spreader with a frightened cry,
Or a stout bulwark and a sheltering tower?

Lord! Here and now into Thy hands I give
    My hours – my crowded working hours – yes, all
The varied hours that I may have to live –
    Watching – asleep – at morn – or evenfall;
With all hours Thine I shall be still with Thee
If that dark dreaded hour should come to me.

# TO THE AXIS

The World was looking on – my lords of Conquest;
   All the World was looking on with sickened glance,
When your wheels went rumble-rumble over daffodils of
      Holland –
   Went crushing down the lilies of France.

The World is looking on – my lords of Robbery,
   As you total up your evil-gotten gains;
As your wheels go rumble-rumble over Europe's starving
      children, –
   Over Europe bound and helpless in her chains.

But *wheels turn again* – my lords of Murder;
   Justice is still alive; her chariots wait;
And she will pay back double what you cost the World in
      trouble –
   Her hour is coming soon – or coming late.

Then – like the whirling dust before the whirlwind;
   Then – as the chaff about the threshing floor;
Why – *then* – my lords of Violence and Lying
   You shall be found no more!

*Chapter Nine*

## DAYS OF DANGER

THE SEASON WAS SO MILD THAT IN NOVEMBER mignonette was still a'flourish. Bees continued to visit it for I saw them thronging the blossoms, and each bee had on each of his thighs a coral bag the exact colour of mignonette.

In the wood the seasons met. Violets were blooming, and here and there we found primroses. The streams had burst their bounds and ran anywhere. From the top of the wood we saw a heron wading in the flooded meadow below. White gulls hovered above, and sometimes swam in the much enlarged mill stream.

Our national affairs showed no marked signs of straightening out. Disasters, assaults and perils had fallen upon us, and Mr. Churchill said: "All we have got to show is survival, and an increasing strength, and an inflexible will to win."

Our thoughts and prayers which had been drawn out towards one European country after another, now centred round Greece – attacked by Italy. The wrongs to be righted were becoming so numerous; the power to do it seemed to be so long in gathering the necessary impetus. John, like many another, could not help exclaiming bitterly about our wasted years. Those careless, do as you like – when you like and how you like – years, when the enemy was piling up armaments, and we were wasting our substance on things which never could enable us to be true to our responsibilities. We had lost the Past, and that we might not lose the Future we must work as we had never worked before, doing all we could to keep our sense of urgency at boiling point.

The starry skies of November were becoming more and more devil-ridden. The principal target had for a long time been London, and now came the first mass raid on a provincial city – Coventry. This shocked and grieved everybody in a new way. The terrorizing quality of aerial warfare came nearer and nearer. The brave words uttered by those who had helped in rescue work, the sense of eternity which was now most truly with us, seemed to draw us daily, almost hourly, into conscious fellowship with the heart of things.

At church our little band drew closer together. We lingered on the steps after the service, telling each other of helpful things which had come our way. Most of us admitted that we were not entirely immune from fear. The noise and the darkness made the situation alarming. The Deaconess said that after committing spirit, soul and body to the keeping of God she left it at that. Another friend confessed that when the worst times were on she wandered miserably about the house; another lady who lived with two deaf sisters said it was having to listen for all three which made the nights rather unrestful.

The villages around us had visitations. One small hamlet was aroused by bombs, and the word went round that parachutists were landing in a field known as the Forty Acre. The Home Guard, chiefly men of the farm and byre, were soon running at top speed up the steep lane, but the alarm turned out to be a false one. There were no parachutists in the Forty Acre, only a plane in flames lay among the tussocks of grass. The German pilot lay crumpled on his side some distance away, and someone covered his body with a sheet of corrugated iron.

One night just before ten o'clock John, Bunty and I sat by the fire and talked about going to bed, when the most devastatingly terrific bang I have ever heard hurled itself at the windows, shook the walls and the roof and the floor, and seemed in some strange manner to come up through the settee upon which I was sitting and hit my spine!

This was followed by other explosions with only seconds between each, and then was succeeded by silence so complete and so intense that it seemed as though the Village was holding its breath. John thought we had better go to our agreed refuge – the space behind the green baize door. No sooner had we got there than he said he must go out.

Something like panic seized my legs and I said: "Oh, don't go, a bomb might fall on you!"

But he had gone and Bunty, who was standing on the back doorstep listening, said: "Don't be silly!" (This was said in the calmly kind voice she uses when she thinks I may be going to disgrace the family.) "Don't be silly, Mother – I may have to go to the First Aid Post!"

Nothing could be heard but the drone of planes, and after a while John returned to say he had fallen in with two Fire Watchers who told him that bombs had been dropped close to the Cottage Hospital. Some people had had their windows shattered but nobody seemed to have been hurt.

The next afternoon when Bunty went to her usual Red Cross work she heard how our little house of healing stood up under its ordeal. It is literally what it claims to be – a Cottage Hospital – for it was made out of several cottages standing in a row on a strata of the hillside which overlooks the Frome valley, and is just at the top of the steep winding descent known as Rosemary Lane.

Naturally, our hospital has no wide stairs nor spacious corridors, but many unsuspected steps and narrow passages, none of them too well lit. When the bombs dropped electricity failed, and it was a perilous and delicate business getting the patients down to the ground floor by lantern light.

The babies in their cradles were already in their usual night apartment – the Matron's sitting-room. Rheumaticky Mr. Snell nipped out of bed at the first bang and was downstairs before anyone. Mr. Simms was longer because his nurse could not induce one of his bedroom slippers to stay on. It kept falling off until she discovered that in the darkness she was putting it on his hand.

The Night Nurse and Sister offered their arms to Mrs. Lavington. Mrs. Lavington was stout. She had just been prepared for an operation to take place on the morrow. Her hair was scraped back and done up in a top-knot; and wearing a flowered kimono dressing-gown, she looked exactly like a Chinese doll.

The more phlegmatic of the male patients refused to stir. That terrifying few seconds was over and, as they rightly judged, nothing more happened. They made jeering and contemptuous noises when their companions returned to the ward and were helped into bed again. Only a few seconds – but seconds, so Nurse Bland told them, could be rather dreadful.

Nurse Bland had just gone off duty, and was on her way home along the Tyning, when she saw a lurid light in the sky. Now it was rather queer, but only that day in the Roman City she had purchased a waterproof hood with bomb flaps to fasten over the ears, at which she had laughed saying she should never want them. At the sound of the first bomb she threw herself among the herbage on the steep bank, pulled down her bomb flaps, and breathlessly counted seventeen explosions, as she waited for the place to be blown up.

Numerous small fires began to appear in gardens, fields and open spaces, as quantities of incendiaries had also been dropped. Dozens fell upon the pig farm.

It was thought the Germans were being chased and that they dropped their bombs to get away. Nurse Bland had counted correctly. There were seventeen bomb craters, all in open spaces, and it seemed amazing to us that they could fall as they did, nicely spaced, away from dwellings and buildings, where they could do little harm.

The next day was sunny and alluring. The air was soft, the weir tossed its white foam with the yellow fleck in it, and the shining river swirled merrily on its way. Larks were singing above the Church Fields, and it was hard to believe such a joyous morning could follow such a terror-striking night.

The Deaconess had some relatives living at Pipehouse, a hamlet in our parish, where an incendiary dropped on their rabbit hutch. The father of the family rushed out and secured the rabbit. The children were rather frightened at first, but were quite joyfully excited when their old friend Mr. Tring, the policeman, marched in without knocking and told them to put on their things at once and go wherever they could. Unexploded bombs were close at hand and might go off at any moment.

That family, and all the other families in the hamlet, trekked out in the mist of a November night. They were given accommodation in the Village. Those whose houses were already full made squeezing room for one more, and very kindly lent all sorts of things which the population of Pipehouse, so suddenly evacuated, had forgotten to take with it. After some days the exiles were allowed to go back, although the bomb disposal squad was still looking for unexploded bombs.

Fire watching in the Village now became an organized service. Among those who patrolled our corner were Mr. Bates and Mr. Webster, both of them possessing keen eyesight, but both being rather hard of hearing. Mr. Bates was always accompanied by his black cat, a lady with a strong attachment to Mr. Bates and a hatred of almost everyone else.

The cat's green eyes could be seen looming out of the darkness, a short space between her and the two worthies who were usually in deep – and exceedingly loud – conversation. Up and down, up and down they went, and it was they who saw and reported the Light in the Window. As they stood upon the slope not far from the Rectory, turning and looking back upon the Village, they distinctly saw a bright light shining unashamed into the pitch black darkness.

As a community we have been exceedingly strict with ourselves over the black-out. If through accident someone turns on the light in an unshuttered room, that someone rushes in a frenzy to draw curtains and drag down the blinds. If some little shaft of light should penetrate at the side, or over the top of the black-out, the householder is approached in the nicest manner possible and there the matter ends.

Mr. Bates, Mr. Webster and the black cat stood staring at that square of golden light. Then they marched solemnly down to the Village to do their obvious duty. As they went down the hill they lost sight of the light. They plodded carefully round the lane, taking in the backs as well as the fronts of the houses, stumbling over pig buckets and slipping down concealed steps. They almost fell into the stone trough into which the spring gushes loudly – only Mr. Bates and Mr. Webster could not hear it, and the black cat could not warn them – but they did not find the light.

Deciding that the householder had extinguished it while they were descending the hill, they went back to their beat. And there was the light again, bright and unwinking as before. The two men, being nonplussed, went to knock up Mr. Wendover the Warden. Mrs. Wendover came to the door. A light in the Village! Mrs. Wendover had been aware of that for the last fortnight at least, and had wondered what in the world the fire-watchers were thinking about!

Mrs. Wendover's voice "carried" so well that next-door neighbours came out and added their opinion that the policeman should be put on the job. But even Mr. Tring, though he tried hard, was unable to locate the light which intermittently but quite frequently, shone forth into the darkness and, as Mrs. Wendover said, might be the cause of the Village being blown up.

She strongly suspected there was a Quisling amongst us, signalling to the Germans. Were there not many stories of such things? At last a very Big Pot indeed came out from the Roman City to investigate, but that night the light was not shining, and never has shone since, so that the mystery remained, and still remains, unsolved.

In those stirring days raids on our City of the West were becoming of almost nightly occurrence, and I felt much anxiety about my mother's household. Many parts of the city were being evacuated, and Mrs. Wills came to see me once more. She was impressed by our self-contained flat, and went away saying she would consider whom she could send to us. So Mrs. Nonesuch and I put everything in order and tried to prepare ourselves for whatever might take place.

The week-end passed. For us it was uneventful, except that when Edward came he told us the City of the West was "knocked sick". Park Street was down, many beautiful churches were destroyed, the Bishop's Palace and a good many chapels were burnt to ashes. We heard their old familiar names spoken with regret, and what beautiful names our forbears gave to the Houses they built for the worship of Almighty God! The names of holy men were freely used, and also the names of holy places. Bethel, Zion, Salem, and Bethesda – what favourites these were! How they reminded even passers-by of the mighty transactions which had taken place between God and the wayward sons of men.

For me the Chapel with Five Porches held memories. It was held in veneration by our elders, for there ministered the man who, in his generation, stood forth pre-eminently as a man of faith, and of answered prayer. For long years a German – George Muller by name, honoured, and was honoured by, our City of the West. Outwardly that chapel was bare and unbeautiful, plain with Quaker-like simplicity within, yet to many souls it had been a quickening place and the very gate of Heaven.

Whenever we heard the raiders going over in waves I could not help being worried about the safety of my own people. John, too, had many anxious moments for he had a branch business in the city, and the staff, two of whom lived over the premises, were constantly in his thoughts. Miss Colston, the manageress, had many stirring experiences. During this particular week-end she went with her sister to a service on the Sunday evening at a nearby church where the Bishop was preaching. He had just begun his sermon when a violent explosion sent the whole congregation, including the Bishop and the Vicar, to the crypt.

It was bitterly cold, and tea was handed round. There was a piano, and there was community singing of old hymns which could be sung without a book. Gathering them into a corner Miss Colston's sister took special charge of the children. She told them stories, taught them little happy, rollicking verses, and kept them so busy that there was a general sigh of dismay when quite suddenly, although there had been no All Clear, the whole congregation was told to leave the crypt.

Everybody wondered why! As soon as they were outside they knew. The church was on fire! The scene was terrible – sky almost as light as day, searchlights out, flares burning, dozens of planes circling overhead, gun-fire deafening, shrapnel falling, explosive bombs and incendiaries dropping all around.

The clatter between the explosions, Miss Colston said, was like thousands of tin trays and saucepans falling. She ran towards home, and literally went through fire and through water that night, for water was surging along the street like a river and buildings were blazing around her in every direction. The garage was alight, the cinema was alight, the furniture store was alight, the leather shop was alight, the chemist's was alight, the wine shop was alight, the museum was alight, a wing of the University was alight, Princes Theatre was alight – in fact it all seemed alight.

She found their three-way corner full of firemen negotiating fire-escapes and hose-pipes. The windows of John's business premises were smashed, and the door was jammed so tightly she could not get in until a policeman broke it open, but otherwise the place had met with no harm.

Miss Colston laughed a little as she said: "We were thankful we were still alive and able to be of use." It appeared that she and her sister used all their rations in providing refreshment for wardens and firemen at intervals all night.

Even after all this I received a reassuring telephone message from my mother and felt comparatively at rest about her, but the next night – Monday – the raiders came again, though by a different route, for here in our Village we were not aware of it. I was sitting writing letters when the Deaconess came to inquire whether we had any tidings. She added that her own relatives who were in the same district had phoned that morning at four a.m. asking that someone might fetch them as things had become too bad for them to remain.

My head began to whirl round! Mrs. Nonesuch was just about to go shopping, and I ran to the kitchen and asked her to go straight to Mr. Bagshaw's at the garage and phone.

She returned to say that my people had their things all packed ready to come, but that they could not get a car. Now, Mr. Bagshaw had arranged to fetch them. They hoped to be with us during the afternoon.

It was seven o'clock in the evening when they arrived – my mother, Griselda and their young maid, Olivia. They were three hours on a journey which in normal times takes only one. By circuitous routes, for many roads were blocked and roped off, Mr. Bagshaw had at last got clear of the city.

Explosives, incendiaries and time bombs had dropped in their road, each side of and at the back, but not on their house. Worn out and heavy-eyed, but smiling still, my mother spoke of God's overshadowing mercy.

As Bunty and I took them upstairs, and Mrs. Nonesuch took charge of Olivia, we realized that our long anticipated, often dreaded evacuees had come to us at last. And far from being strangers whose requirements and habits might have found us wanting, they were our very own folk.

# CITY OF THE WEST

City! For centuries thy sons have sailed
 With stout Sebastian to the Polar Sea,
Seeking New Worlds until with joy they hailed
 The far-off outlines of Eternity.

City! When England's soul had gone astray,
 A prophet rose and cried on Kingswood Hill,
Till fire which warmed John Wesley in his day
 Kindled in thee a beacon burning still.

And thou hast not forgotten, favoured town –
 So rich wert thou in those who greatly dare –
That man of God who long on Ashley Down
 Proved and proclaimed the mighty power of prayer.

Storm clouds are dark, skies black and overcast,
 Death and destruction knock upon thy door;
But now, proud City with the honoured past,
 Thy hour of high adventure comes once more.

# WOMEN OF BRITAIN

Hark! It is the summons of
    The bugle of the Lord.

He who called the men of Britain
    To become His living sword
Sounds once more His royal challenge,
    Calls with no uncertain claim
To the women of Great Britain
    To become His living flame.

They have heard it! They have heard
    That compelling mighty word.
They have answered in their thousands –
    Body willing – spirit stirred!

Up with haste the British women
    Rise responsive to the call –
Women stout and women slender –
    Women queenly, women small.

Proud – ah! Proud – the British women;
    Quick – how quick – their hasting feet
March from parlour and from palace,
    Castled gate and battered street.

Women young and women old,
Women shy and women bold,
    Bringing for an offering
Hands to lend,
And backs to bend –
Women with their lives to spend
    In the service of their King.

They are willing! They are willing!
　　British women here and now
Drive with skill Britannia's lorries,
　　Run to guide Britannia's plough;
They will mind Britannia's children,
　　Scrub, and shop, and wash, and mend,
Crochet, knit, and sew for Britain
　　Till her hour of need shall end.

Swift to do Britannia's bidding –
　　Never asking why, nor when;
Toiling in Britannia's kitchens
　　They will feed her fighting men;
In machine shops, in munitions,
　　Toiling hard for Britain's sake;
Nothing – *nothing* – British women
　　Cannot – will not – undertake.

They are giving! They are giving
Time and treasure, strength and skill;
Smooth hands – rough hands –
Soft hands – tough hands –
Resolute and toiling still.

Gently on Britannia's wounded,
　　Free from hurry as from fear,
They are laying hands of healing,
　　Hands of sympathy and cheer.

Yes, and loyal British women,
　　With the faith which understands
From their beds of pain and anguish
　.Lift up faithful praying hands.

Can they fail? The splendid answer
 Thunders over land and sea:
*Britain cannot die while Britons*
 *Work and fight for victory!*

They have harkened to the summons of
 The bugle of the Lord,
He who called the men of Britain
 To become His living sword!
They have taken up the challenge
 And acknowledging His claim:

British women! British women!
 *You* shall be His living flame!

## Chapter Ten

### THE DOWNS AND THE UPS

WE HAD A BUSY AND INTERESTING TIME GETTING our home affairs running to fit in with the new arrangements. This meant a complete change round, and re-adjustment of most of our ways. We had exactly doubled the number of persons in our household, and more than doubled the number of rooms in constant use.

Olivia liked Mrs. Nonesuch and gave her graphic descriptions of the Awful Nights experienced in the City of the West: the camp-beds in kitchen and passages; frequent descents into the cellar; no water; no light – only candles flaring.

These recitals amused my sister, because Olivia's snores from the kitchen had kept Griselda awake when the planes didn't. Often, after a truly frightening session, Olivia asked innocently: "Did Jerry come over last night, Miss?" She was, however, a very quick, efficient and useful little maid, and with her help the domestic affairs began to run fairly well.

Griselda undertook the shopping, now a daily task involving long waits and many disappointments. Mr. Hazeldean's shop was always crowded. The young men and women who served had need of more than all the patience they possessed, and their behaviour was an example of resourcefulness and good humour.

It is true that Mr. Bing had to run his hand through his hair fairly often, when customers could not be brought to understand that only half a pound of biscuits could be allowed per week to each household; nor that Mr. Bing could not produce sausages and pork pies at will! He had to explain to Mrs. Wendover that, as her grandson had gone into the Navy, she was no longer able to draw his rations in spite of the fact that all his civvy clothes and his locked trunk resided at her house.

The days when soft-spoken young men waited on one's doorstep for orders and kindly reminded one of the commodities one had omitted; the days when one was encouraged and invited to run up a big bill for groceries – these times were over. Syrup, marmalade, bottled coffee – one had almost given up hope of seeing such things again, and when Griselda happened to obtain one orange for each of us she came home absurdly elated.

She had to wait at the butcher's while a telephone customer held a long and fatuous conversation with Mr. Merriman. Jock from Plymouth and Edward from Southampton emerged from "the back" each wearing a long, bibbed, and exceedingly dirty apron slipped by tapes over their heads, and Jock swung by the legs a dead and skinny cockerel. Mr. Merriman, who had at last finished with the telephone, received them as though they had been plenipotentiaries, and under his instructions Griselda obtained a very, very small rabbit and some cat's meat.

We were now entreated by the Government to save bones and not to waste bread, but we were all of us so busy that only my mother found time to listen to the news. It was she who kept us informed concerning the Libyan campaign, and the utter ruin in the offices and warehouses of the London publishers. When I heard later that all stocks of my books – twenty-five titles – had been burned, together with the blocks and original wrapper-designs by Margaret Tarrant, I felt concerned, but it did not seem to come so close to me as the increasing shortage of eggs and onions.

December was mild and sunny. On Christmas Day we had pink roses and mignonette on the tea table. We also had an amazing iced cake sent from Canada. We had raisins, sugar and cream cheese from Australia, and a large, round, very fruity confection from New Zealand. I wish those generous unknown friends of mine could have looked in and seen us sitting around the table – the same children, the same parents, who have formed our Christmas circle for so many years. The guests brought their own butter (rationing would not allow it to be otherwise), but how we all enjoyed that thoroughly un-wartime tea!

We were still being told by our leaders that there were hard times ahead. We were still facing the enemy alone. The only bright spot seemed to be that we were driving the Italians out of Abyssinia, and it appeared that the first of all the dispossessed to be restored was the little dark-skinned Emperor whom the League of Nations had so badly let down.

We were especially interested in him because he had for a long time made his home in the Roman City next door to Bunty's Irish friend, Mary O'Neill. The youngest of the Abyssinian clan – a little boy of five – sometimes went for tea with Mary O'Neill. He stood on her doorstep one Christmas morning jumping up and down saying: "I have come to wish you a Happy Christmas, and – please – can I see the little bird?"

He ran in, and the little bird, a budgerigar named Chilipeke, came out of his cage and sat on the small Ethiopian head. Mary O'Neill said there was great rejoicing in the house next door when the Emperor was recalled to his own country. His long and humiliating exile was, we hope, helped by the sympathy of the English people.

I stood once in the principal street of the Roman City and saw Haille Selassie come out of the Post Office. Multitudes surged around his car so that he could scarcely get into it. With great dignity the dark turbanned head acknowledged the sympathetic greeting of the crowd. I heard a French woman standing near me say sadly: "Ah! we made him too much hope."

In such days it seemed the height of heartlessness to think about the January sales which were just then in full swing, but it had become imperative that we should replenish the china pantry. Alas! Of all the smashers who ever smashed I think that our young Olivia would have taken first prize. Cups without handles – jugs without lips – chipped plates and tumblers now confronted us at every meal.

We possess very little silver, but pretty china has been one of our extravagances. We have, I am afraid, sometimes bought small jugs and odd plates for the sheer pleasure of using them. But now our reserves were fast diminishing. It was apparently so easy, when a glass was broken, to get another from the top shelf of the pantry that when I climbed from chair to dresser myself, thinking to bring out of my treasure things new and old, most of the treasure had disappeared.

Mrs. Nonesuch made an expressive face when she saw the new, cheap, but pretty tea-set of plain green which we brought home with us. She hoped Olivia would leave off having "those banging fits", or very little of anything would be left intact. Mrs. Nonesuch was not feeling very well just then; she had pains in her side and she complained of a bad back. She said Olivia dropped potato peelings all over the kitchen floor, and did not scrub the sink, and made muddles in the maids' sitting-room. She added: "All the same there's a war on, and I shall get through sometime."

But the next Sunday morning Olivia came to my door to tell me Mr. Nonesuch had been up to say his wife was ill and could not come.

Olivia's face was bright and shining, her apron supernaturally clean. She intimated that anything I would like her to do she would be pleased to undertake.

Full of foreboding I rose and went downstairs. I think I knew at once what had happened. The campaign for which we had so carefully planned – through no fault of anybody – had broken down, and I felt as though I had been defeated on both fronts.

Mrs. Nonesuch proved to be too ill to come back. She went into our Cottage Hospital for observation, and after treatment it was imperative that she should have a long rest. To Bunty and to me this was a staggering blow. Our concern for her and her concern for us was very great. She entreated me to try to get someone else who would take all responsibility. And this to us was hard and heavy tidings, for reading between the lines we knew something which had been precious and greatly valued had come to an end. Well! I have lost good maids before, but never in all my experience have I lost a helper of the quality of Mrs. Nonesuch.

John's sensible remark that "You cannot get rid of your troubles by running away from them" was true. The hard fact had to be faced – the house had to be kept going, and mine must be the hand at the helm. Olivia could not be depended upon to carry much of the load, but we should have been infinitely worse off without her.

She broke something nearly every day, but she washed saucepans and prepared vegetables and did some of the cleaning. Cooking the meals and washing up after them took most of the time.

Also, just at this time people began coming to the door to ask whether we had rooms to let. Some of them were distressingly situated; women whose homes were gone, and – not surprisingly – nerves gone too, so that they could not feel safe at night in the City of the West. How often we heard the plea: "My husband is away all day at his work. Could you let us have just one room where we could sleep?"

Situated as we were we could not help in this way, but many houses were divided up, kitchens and bathrooms were shared, and persons who had never thought to let, nor to occupy space in someone else's home, learned to put up their horses amicably. War is a great leveller, and it can be a simplifier, too.

Just now, however, a bad spell of ice and snow complicated matters for everybody. Griselda trudged off in rubber boots to do the daily shopping, while Olivia and I cleaned the rooms. But oh! how dark were the mornings. John and Bunty were off for their train long before we dared remove the black-out. The hall and stairs were bound to be in semi-darkness because of the glass dome above. It is a wonder we did not knock our heads against the doors, and fall headlong down the bathroom stairs several times a day.

Olivia was so small she could not reach to unveil the kitchen windows, and it was a most gloomy thing to go after breakfast into that dimly-lit workshop littered all over with trays and saucepans and dirty crockery. Any attempt on our part to empty teapots and to scrape plates, ready for washing-up, met with so much antagonism from Olivia that Griselda and I decided to leave her to it, and get on with bed-making and bedroom tidying.

The light when it actually came revealed that the most deplorable conditions prevailed everywhere. The situation which baffled me most was the universal presence of *Bits*! They stuck on the carpets and on the stair; on the hearth-rug and on each chair; on woollen jumpers and on our hair. Bits – bits – bits seemed everywhere. In vain I went around the house with a dustpan and a brush; in vain I beat, brushed, pulled and picked. Those bits, and others like them, were determined to stay in every place where it was possible for bits to find a lodging. Mrs. Nonesuch must have had magic in her touch for she had contrived to keep the bits under control – and frankly, as far as bits were concerned, I had to own myself beaten.

Soon, however, I had other things besides bits to show me what manner of woman I was. John, who had had a troublesome cold, was suddenly laid up. He could speak only with difficulty, pausing between every word. But he would not, he said, have the Lady Doctor in. If I sent for her he would refuse to see her. There were few things he would refuse to do for me, but to have the Lady Doctor was one of them!

Being afraid to make his breathing even worse, I agreed and said that, of course, Helen was out of the question! Helen was a friend of Bunty's – a wonderfully capable and efficient young woman who had taken on the work of our doctor when he put on khaki and went to serve the Forces.

Her father did allow his daughter, Nurse Inchfawn, to take his temperature, and she pronounced it only slightly above normal. He agreed to stay in bed and in one atmosphere as his ailment was surprisingly like laryngitis or bronchitis – we weren't sure which! Those who have ever tried to run a house short of staff will realize how greatly meals upstairs can complicate matters – how many trays must go up and down, and how many little attentions need to be given in one day – to say nothing of time taken in sitting with the patient.

To stop John from talking I read aloud to him from "The Trumpet Major" – that part of the story where Hardy describes how the miller made ready for Matilda; but he laughed so much at the description of Captain Bob Loveday painting the gig that his cough became really alarming and the reading ceased.

Things were going queerly altogether just then. I was feeling down and flattened out and old and cross all the time, when Michael, coming to the back door one morning to ask what vegetables were required, paused a moment and said solemnly:

"I know of a good maid."

I said: "Michael, do you, really?"

He said: "I do – a good hard-working girl. She is leaving Mrs. Frobisher's where she has been for seven years, and she is wanting a quiet place."

To myself I thought that a "quiet place" was among the things which had gone off the market. Also, I must admit, I had no hope at all that this paragon would come to us. I knew only too well of the hosts of mistresses who would swoop down upon her the moment it was known that she was available, but I asked her name and told Michael to tell her to come and see me. He replied that her name was Amaryllis, and that she would be calling on Saturday.

I flew upstairs to tell John. He sat up solemnly and said: "You are to engage her! Now, mind what I say – it is my wish that you should engage her. I know her by sight very well, and she will take the load off you."

On the appointed day Amaryllis came to see me. I met her at the door, a fresh-coloured, comfortable-looking young woman, with eyes as blue as the sky is over her own county of Clare. I showed her the rooms, and strangely enough it appeared that Amaryllis had once been in service in this very house and knew it well. She agreed to come to us in three weeks' time!

That three weeks with emancipation at the end of, seemed as nothing. So greatly can the spirit over-ride body that, with that hope in view, the work seemed immediately less arduous to us all; though in reality there was more to be done, as Amaryllis' bedroom had to be papered and got ready for her reception. I was arranging matters with Mr. Flower when our friends the gas men arrived put in a gas fire. They were barely introduced to the room when Olivia's head appeared at the top of the back stair. A gentleman had called who said he must see me, and she had shown him into the study.

Thinking it was probably someone to ask whether we had rooms to let, I went down and found Mr. Harmer, our Civil Defence Officer. The last time he came it was to fit our gas-masks; now he had called to advise us concerning incendiary bombs. He asked us whether we possessed a stirrup pump. We did not, but we had one on order. Mr. Harmer said it should be kept in the conservatory, with a long-handled shovel and a bucket of sand. In the porch we had better keep a bucket of water and a sack of sand. In each of two places on the landing there should be a bucket of sand. Mr. Harmer asked whether we had a trap-door to our roof, and I said: "Yes."

"Then you should keep a ladder just beneath it." He made a note that we also possessed an extension ladder which we were prepared to lend to our neighbours in case of fire.

At this point Mr. Harmer, sitting with his note-book in front of him, looked at me very hard across the table and said: "Where is your nearest hydrant?"

I replied: "Opposite the Rectory, but Mr. Flower will show you!"

"No! No!" said Mr. Harmer. "I know very well where the hydrants are – I'm trying to find out whether *you* know, and as it happens you are right. Yours is opposite the Rectory. I shall give you a good mark for that! You are about the only person who has given me a correct answer."

I must admit that I only knew because I had once seen Mr. Flower performing with a long-handled key in a hole in the road outside our garden door.

After telling me his difficulties in getting fire watchers, because only the doddering and the decrepit seemed willing to do it, Mr. Harmer departed, but he left me with a lift in my spirit. He was doing his job so well and with such courtesy. His own house was accommodating evacuees – twin boys. George and Ned were well known – the brightest-eyed, neatest lads in the Village, and as alike as two peas. They came collecting our waste paper, and often I met them on my walks abroad. We stood and we chattered together, and I only hope they did not know that I was never quite sure which was George and which was Ned.

Our affairs now began to take shape. The bedroom was finished and as clean as hands could make it. The back stair-carpet was taken up and beaten and put down again. We had covers new and gay made for settee and chairs in the maids' sitting-room – and on a Monday morning, at twelve of the clock, Amaryllis walked in, and with her coming our household acquired the benefits of a New Order.

The difference which one pair of hands made to us was almost unbelievable. Olivia – with her "new playmate", as John called Amaryllis – rose to the zenith of her powers, and her face was as bright as the sun on Easter Day. As for me I was able to sit in the sun, and get out my manuscripts, papers and note-books to see whether anything at all was left in me!

# PEACE MAY COME TO EARTH AGAIN!

It will not always be so dark o'mornings.
    We may not always be without a maid.
We shall not always supplicate for syrup,
    Nor beg upon our knees for marmalade.

We shall not always have to scrimp with sugar,
    And call five times at butcher's for the meat.
We shall not always wrestle – waking – sleeping –
    With how to get and cook enough to eat.

Eggs will come back, with butter, and with bacon,
    Cheese, honey, fruit, and yellow cream in clot.
We shall not always have to count the tea leaves
    And put them grudgingly within the pot.

We shall not always have our night's rest broken
    By crashing bomb, and hum of hovering plane.
The spring will come – and after that the summer –
    And – who knows?  Peace may come to earth again!

## ENGLAND KEEPS CHRISTMAS

So you will keep a wartime Christmas, England,
    Without your Christmas trees!
Your called-up daughters, serving you, will gladly
    Forego their Christmas ease;
While thousands of your tall sons guard you, England,
    Airborne – and on the seas.
Solemn and silent in green ivied belfries
    Your church bells will not chime;
Your windows densely darkened show no glimpses
    Of any festive time.

And yet, if any nation should keep Christmas,
    Mindful of mercies known – and those unknown –
England, you are that Nation! Uninvaded,
    Still strong, still free, and still not overthrown –
You must keep thankful-hearted Christmas, England,
    Not once forgetting when you bend your knee
The peoples who must sit in fetters, England,
    Across your Channel and your Northern Sea.

Humbly you will keep Christmas, England, knowing
    Its message for a world so wrecked and worn;
Then shall the angels sing: "In England – *England* –
    A Saviour, Christ the Lord, is newly born!"

## Chapter Eleven

### THE VILLAGE IS STIRRED

AFTER THIS THERE WAS A LONG PERIOD OF INACTION, and the Village again lost most of its evacuees. Mrs. Cook, the cheerful young hairdresser from Bond Street, was no more at our beck and call, and she left behind a multitude of lamenting clients. For, truly, Mrs. Cook was "one of the outstanding compensations", so Katie Bannister declared, "of there being a war at all".

Mrs. Cook was billeted in a commodious house where she had the use of a wash-basin with running water, and here she did a brisk business in washes and sets. But to obtain the full glory of Mrs. Cook's attainments you had to have her at home.

At the appointed time she arrived with her attaché-case and was ushered upstairs. She and her client were left in privacy for the space of one hour and the results were astounding. With a wet shampoo, a curling tongs and a hand-drier, Mrs. Cook turned the greasiest, lankiest locks into waves of shining beauty.

While the hand-drier was doing its tedious work, she related stories of noble houses in stately London. It was an inspiring thought that, before Society weddings and other important functions – known to us only by the pictures in the newspapers – Mrs. Cook had washed, and curled the hair of Very Great Ladies, just as she washed and curled the much more humble hair of the Village. It was a severe blow to our complacency when Mrs. Cook's husband decided that London was as safe as any other place.

For a time we decided to wash and set our own hair just as we did before the days of perms and immaculate coiffures. Nevertheless, there comes a time when a professional "trim" is a necessity, and wishing most patriotically to save the petrol which a visit to my own respected Mr. Swift would use, I decided to try a certain Mrs. Briggs who was nearer at hand. My daughter, very reluctantly and against her better judgment, made an appointment for me, and quite hopefully I went.

I was greeted by two young things wearing slacks who chattered incessantly to each other, while one of them slashed cold shampoo over my head, and rubbed it round. I had suggested a very little trim to enable hair to roll up better. The young lady, relating all the time to her colleague a story with certain glamorous details, sheared inches from my hair. And for this I paid half-a-crown.

When I got home there was no set anywhere, though the setting lotion remained in glutinous patches. I washed it all out and Bunty kindly, albeit triumphantly, rang up Mr. Swift.

A neat head really does give one a feeling of satisfaction – a feeling which has in it the same sense of order and rightness which a tidy larder, or an organized linen-cupboard, bestows on the ardent home-maker. My thoughts had, I remember, been wandering around many little trivial things, when they were suddenly and sharply swung to a different plane. One evening John came home with the news that young Patrick McEvoy had "gone down".

How can I describe the feeling which went over the Village? Moved and saddened we had been before; even in peace-time changes come, but now it was as though the spirit of something very rare and precious had been torn up by the roots. Though ours is an inland village we have never been without our links with the sea, but I speak truly when I say that the loss of the battleship *Hood* off Greenland did not touch us so nearly as did the foundering of one small minesweeper somewhere around our coasts with young Patrick McEvoy aboard her.

Patrick was known to us all, chiefly because his main interest in life, up to the time he joined the minesweeping service, was "gipsying". When he was not wandering round and about the Village and the river and the woods, he toured the counties in a horse-drawn caravan, living and travelling with real Romanies. The experiences of his gipsy travels he recorded in "The Gorse and the Briar," a fine mature book for a young man of twenty-five.

The Village in the main thought of Patrick with indulgence, even though "playing at gipsies" was not the usual way of the young gentlemen the Village knew best. *They* went to public schools, and came home wearing clothes cut by city tailors and with the gentleman note in their speech and bearing. Patrick McEvoy did not put himself out to obtain the groomed look of the highly bred. But he was born of artists and of poets. He knew the twilights and the dawnlights, and the colours which lie upon the river's face at all times of the year. He could walk so that birds and beasties did not fear him. He could loiter with the inarticulate and understand them. I think that our lanes, our fields and our Friary Wood may have uttered a lament for the passing of young McEvoy – the lad who knew, loved, listened, and never betrayed their confidence.

The Village suffered other losses. There was George, the baker's young man, a motor dispatch driver who came safely through Dunkirk, but was never heard of after Singapore. There was Alfred who was killed by one of our own land mines near the coast. There was also Pilot Officer Lang – the hero of fifty flights – who was lost over Berlin.

Not long after this our nearest neighbour sailed for India. A quiet restrained man was Mr. Field. Of him the Village said, and meant it: "He's a gentleman!"

Six months of the year he spent in England, and the other six he was engaged in the Indian offices of his firm's publishing house. This time, however, his sojourn at home was much longer as he had to wait his turn for a passage. Then one day he met Bunty and said to her: "Tell your mother that I have been able to get a ship at last, and I am coming in to say good-bye."

That ship was the *Britannia*. It seemed to us such a short while before we heard on the radio that she had been sunk by a surface raider in the Indian Ocean. We waited anxiously for tidings of survivors, but these were few, and Mr. Field's name was not among them. This incident occurring so sharply after the others cast a gloom over us, and now more than ever the Village realized that the war was coming nearer home.

These upheavals, changes and losses all seemed to me to be a call to enter more fully into what it means to plumb the depths and climb the heights of spiritual experience. How could a soul pass through these stirring days and not recognize something of their import?

Not only individuals and families, but whole communities were being carried on the war-tide, right out of their usual dead-level bourne of time and place. One village through which John passes every day on his way to work was specially in our thoughts just then.

The village of Southacre used to be a place of wheat-fields and poppies, skylarks and yellow hammers. One woodland corner of it is the only place I know in the county as the home of the red-backed shrike. Old-world was a term quite naturally, and rightly, applied to it. Indeed, it was one of those villages which remained for a long time in an atmosphere known as almost out-of-the-world.

The residents drew their water from wells; they shopped once a week by walking into Broadwater; they intermarried until it was said there were only two surnames in the parish. And now this village finds itself near enough to the factories for the greater part of its population to be transported daily by bus to do whole or part time industrial work. Up the steep lanes, Sundays and week-days, rumble noisy and evil-smelling vehicles; and Southacre, as we once knew it – fresh and fragrant with the quiet ways of our English ancestors – is no more.

We cannot plumb the depths of our country's trial. We cannot with maps and compasses set a boundary to it. There are thoughts which we need to think, lessons we need to relearn, visions we need to see and never to forget again.

Our England finds herself in the process of remaking. She is getting herself ready for a new England which has yet to be fashioned. We hate to think that the England which our forefathers made for us is passing away; but nothing in it which is worth preserving need ever pass away – that is, if, as a nation, we will to keep it alive.

Let those who love England pray she may never be content to be shut in with her selfishness again.

Let them pray for leaders who will from now onwards lead the British people in being alive, alert, adventurous, and always on guard.

Let them also pray for teachers who will teach England's children that their aim as Britishers must be – not safety, not comfort, not the gaining of material things – but to be worthy, under God, of a bigger share of responsibility for the right conduct of the human race.

# YOU – WHO WILL CARRY OLD ENGLAND ON

We are leaving you a Throne
  Though the other thrones have vanished –
We are leaving you a King
  Unbeaten and unbanished –
You – who will carry old England on
When we are gone –
*When we are gone.*

We are leaving you a Book
  With the mark of truth upon it –
The Book we vowed to honour
  Though we haven't always done it –
You – who will carry old England on
When we are gone –
*When we are gone.*

We are leaving you a Land
  Of glory and of pride –
A land of liberty
  For which our sons have died –
You – who will carry old England on
When we are gone –
*When we are gone.*

This high inheritance
  We leave you – for your own.
These will be *yours! Yours! Yours!*
  This Land – this Book – this Throne –
You – who will carry old England on
When we are gone –
*When we are gone.*

## SINGAPORE

These are the days
Of our grief,
And the days
Of our darkness;
Of humiliation –
When boasting
Must dwindle and wane.

These are also the days
When we see
On the night-black horizon,
Signs – small signs –
Faint and far –
The flickering of a star –
*Our lost star* – rising –
Rising again.

*Chapter Twelve*

## FIRE WATCHERS

ENGLAND NOW BEGAN TO FIRE WATCH IN DEADLY earnest. Practically everybody – able or otherwise – became members of fire-watching parties. Up and down the country garages and club rooms were used as fire posts, but barns and lofts and farm kitchens were more usual in districts like ours, where to lighten the tedium the watchers played chess and darts and draughts and other games.

Of course, solitary fire watchers in private houses usually had odds and ends of work which they were glad to clear up during silent seasons. Reading and mending, and writing letters were among the more favoured occupations, and I heard of one business man who on these night watches regularly got all his accounts ready for posting.

Our old friend Mr. Sands, now in the City of Sarum, was the only one, as far as I know, who beguiled the tedious hours by producing a magazine exclusively for the thirty members of his fire post. This typewritten effusion was known as *The Incendiary*. It had a certified circulation of four copies, and it claimed to be "the journal with the red-hot news".

*The Incendiary* showed many humorous side-lights on the fire watcher's duty and routine. "After signing his name in the book, his next duty is to set up his bed in such a manner that it is in no danger of collapsing under him during the night, and alarming his brother fire watchers. Then he is free to light his pipe – if any – or a cigarette – if any – and engage in pleasant converse with his colleagues till it is time to go to sleep. When he awakes he enters his name in the book again, says: 'Cheerio, my lucky lads!' and pushes off for home, conscious of duty well and truly performed."

To assist in driving home editorial remarks, Mrs. Sands drew some clever cartoons. There were also contributions from the pen of the Cap'n and other members of the post.

The Ministry of Home Security now issued a news-sheet entitled *Midnight Watch,* especially for fire watchers. This was hailed with delight by *The Incendiary,* which boldly claimed to be the pioneer of fire guard journalism. This new Government production was alluded to as "a newly-born rival", and there was much fun in the Sarum post over the little typewritten magazine which took so much flattery to itself.

But those "in the know" were well aware that duty at a fire post is not the most comfortable way of spending the hours of darkness after a day's harassing work. The men who did it were chiefly middle-aged and elderly men who had been looking forward to easier times soon. Now, however, they found themselves obliged to plough through more work and shoulder far greater perplexities than they had had to face in their youth.

It was to men like these – and women also – all over Britain that Mr. Herbert Morrison wrote in *Midnight Watch:* "If you were not there our country would soon be ravaged by huge destructive fires far beyond the power of the fire service to control."

This was the truth which the jovial spirit of *The Incendiary* chose deliberately to ignore. According to Mr. Sands, fire watching was a merry accident and a jolly occupation, and, certainly, his view of the matter made fire watching interesting to his colleagues and brought a laugh to many others including John and me.

This gift of pure "silliness" is not to be despised at any time, but it has proved to be exceedingly valuable in wartime. The British people in spite of all their disappointments, their vicissitudes and their stupid blunders, have never forgotten how to laugh! Best of all they can still laugh at themselves. They are quick to see the funny side even of their most serious problems, and such a spirit is helping more than we realize towards victory. Therefore, salutations to Mr. Sands, and to all other men and women who go about tedious work with twinkles in their eyes.

In our village we were turning our thoughts once more towards the subject of fire watching. Fire Chiefs were being appointed for all districts, and meetings were being held up and down the land. In due time it was announced that our own Fire Chief was going to address a meeting of fire watchers – now dignified by the term Fire Guards – and the meeting was to be held at the Inn.

The Village went, but rather half-heartedly, I fancy, because for such a long time now fire watching had become – so we thought – almost a farce, and if the truth were known had fallen very largely into oblivion. What was the use of losing one's rest when there were no Alerts and nothing doing?

Still, the Village, grumbling and satirical, forsook its gardens and its potato-planting, changed from its working clothes, took its walking sticks and went down the steep hill to the old hostelry, where the London coaches used to swing around the bending road with a flourish and a trumpeting of the posting horn to the hospitable door.

Two rivers – the quiet leisured old Avon and the young hurrying waters of the Frome – meet and join forces in the meadows just below the Inn. The bridge a few yards away was in existence in Leland's day, for he records in the year 1550 that he passed over it on the way from Broadwater to our Roman City.

Close by Miss Moxam has her farm. Cows, so sleek and clean they might have come straight from the bath-tub, were eating the fresh grass with evident delight. At the door of the Inn, and in the yard and waddling all across the road, was a considerable congregation of plump well-favoured ducks. We knew these belonged to the Lady of the Inn who cherishes them, feeds them, and at the proper time calls them and puts them safely to bed.

Steering our way past the ducks we went up a stone stairway on the outside of the building, steadying ourselves with an iron handrail, and entered a low long room extending almost the full length of the Inn. What the Village would do without this oak-beamed room I scarcely know, for it is called into use for all kinds of meetings and village celebrations, from coronations and jubilees to cricket dinners and harvest suppers.

We were all there – the rector, the churchwardens, the school-mistress, the policeman, the postman, the hardworking ladies of the village who rallied at all times around the activities of Mrs. Wills. There was, naturally, a scarcity of young men, but beautifully permed young ladies from Government offices turned up in force, and the presence of Mr. Hazeldean and Mr. Flower added dignity and importance to the proceedings.

The Rector introduced the speaker. He had come from an exacting job in the Roman City to address us on subjects of fire watching and fire fighting. It was feared that possibly we might all have tended to become a little lax in view of the recent lull *(broad smiles)*, but the Rector hoped that Mr. Burnett's address might have the effect of stimulating us to resume our attitude of vigilance *(some sniggers)*.

When Mr. Burnett's time came to address us, he assured us immediately that he, and the authorities in the Roman City, were more than satisfied with the fervour displayed by our Village *(hear! hear! from the front seats, and much, stamping of feet at the back)*. There was, however, a tendency in some districts to lapse into a complacency which was completely unjustified, and therefore it had been decided, regretfully, to apply compulsion to all villages including ours *(the silence could be felt)*.

Mr. Burnett seemed grieved that there was now no stamping nor clapping. He said solemnly we could take it from him that Hitler would be sure to have a smack at us – yes, he would, no matter how many of us held a different opinion.

"Did we," he asked, "consider ourselves entirely free from the danger of bombing, and the threat of invasion?"

No one answered, but the ducks beneath the window set up a loud and protracted quacking, beginning on a crescendo note and sinking to a slow diminuendo.

At the end of the meeting some questions were asked about stirrup pumps, and Mr. Burnett pleaded with us all to examine and use ours at least once a fortnight. The Rector also told a doleful story about the stirrup pump which was kept in the church porch. When fetched hurriedly on one occasion it was found to be faulty – all it would do was to drench the operator, and that pretty thoroughly, which the Rector thought was rather a mean thing for a church stirrup pump to do.

John remembered that our own stirrup pump was in the old wood house, its rubber piping wound round and round itself just as it came from the ironmonger's, and he decided there and then that he must have it out and try it as soon as we got home.

As we came away from the meeting we were given a booklet – *The Fire Guards' Handbook.* Mrs. Wendover was reading hers aloud to her husband as they went down the steps, and those who were near enough heard that the first duty of a Fire Guard is to prevent fire; that one should wear old clothes; carry a few pennies in one's pocket; know where the nearest telephone is; keep calm and act quickly.

As we always do whenever we attend any Village function we fell in with acquaintances whom we seldom meet at any other time, and now outside the Inn we chattered together, and stood watching the fire engine drawing up water from the river where the village crew in the National Fire Service was at practice.

I should think there could be no more pleasant place for the gathering of village folk than that open space before the Inn. The light was still golden behind the wooded hills, and these, because we were at river level, towered high to right and left of us.

The ducks were now waddling along the meadow path towards the river, and the Lady of the Inn had just come to call them to bed. The hour was late by the clock though still early by the sun, and most of us decided to go home. On the whole we were not very sure whether we had not been wasting our time to give attention to a subject which appeared to be almost a dead letter.

"Hitler has plenty to do in Russia!"

"The *Luftwaffe* knows better than to come over here!"

These were the sort of remarks which the Village made as it went home; there were also comments on the easterly winds, and the coldness of nights and mornings, now that the extra hour had been added to Summer Time.

A wonderfully windy day was the last Saturday in April, very bright and light; the wind still easterly and keen, but with a shining clearness in the air which made the grass beside the river very green, and the water like a dark mirror.

Bunty was out on her bicycle all the morning, for after three months of Red Cross work at our Cottage hospital she was taking a holiday. This was punctuated by dental attention, vaccination, and certain inoculations, before starting her training to become a State Registered Nurse.

For a long time she was pulled two ways. Her interest in the Cottage Hospital was intense. Like a little world shut in upon itself it radiated and throbbed with all the interest common to humanity – birth, life allied with weakness, pain, and sometimes death.

The patients themselves were so varied in requirement and disposition. The friends and relations of the patient coming always to and fro brought with them fresh surges from the great sea of affairs. For the Matron and her staff there were difficulties and problems and undercurrents, but underneath and over everything trailed this enfolding glory – the desire to serve the sick.

Yet how well I could understand that during those three months, when she was often baffled by her own ignorance and inefficiency, my daughter should decide to go the whole way and make nursing, not only a career, but a vocation.

Now, I was beginning to realize how war plucks up by the roots our small quiet flowers of comfort and ease. Home life cannot now mean unbroken circles, nor shut-in-ness to our own deeply absorbing affairs. War thrusts us away from life-long habits, but this does not entirely mean impoverishment. I realized, too, that changes can make our selfish hearts flow with deeper, wider sympathy for our fellows. Upheavals can draw us towards new recognitions of the Love and Wisdom which moves so unerringly in every tide, and beats upon every shore.

# NIGHT DUTY

The moon is on night duty clothed in light.
The stars are on night duty every night.

The wind is on night duty – and the sea
Sleeps not, nor rests, but labours ceaselessly.

Soldiers are on night duty. Sailors keep
Faithful and fearless vigil o'er the deep.

Nurses are on night duty – proud to be
Watchers – with pain and death for company.

Myriads are on night duty – eyes unknown
Watch – lest our England should be overthrown.

What right have I – when my poor prayers are said –
Night after night to climb into my bed?

## Chapter Thirteen

### RAIDS ON THE ROMAN CITY

WE WERE THANKFUL FOR THAT APRIL INTERLUDE, and on the last Saturday of the month I sat with the carnations in our small sun parlour, while Bunty went out on her bicycle returning Red Cross aprons and caps to friends who had kindly lent her supplementary garments. Her own uniform she took to the Commandant, who would pass it on to a new member.

In the afternoon we had Bunty's friend, Kathleen, and her two-year-old son Angus for tea. By that time it was warm enough to take our tea tray out of doors. Angus strutted about and picked daisies. He sprawled on the grass, rolling over and over, with Bunty and his mother pulling and pushing him. Never had we been more light-hearted, never had we, or the woodpecker, laughed more loudly.

The evening was peaceful and when John came from his business we strolled about for quite a while. He is always glad when the week-end comes, for life in wartime is hard for business men with all the younger men gone.

We went to bed that night by daylight, and I had fallen into my first sleep, when over the peaceful valley, ominous and slowly, sounded the long banshee-like wail of the siren.

Almost immediately the banging began. My first feeling was

one of annoyance – then of dread. I sat up. John was dragging on his clothes. Through the wide bay window saw great lights flaring in the sky and dropping slowly earthward, not in one place only but in many directions – over Broadwater, over Southacre, over Hayes Wood, over the Roman City, and twenty miles away over the City Of the West.

By this time I had found my shoes and my dressing-gown. The glass in the roof rattled and the whole house shook. Bunty and Amaryllis appeared on the landing, and the back door bell rang a loud peal. It was our neighbours, Mr. and Mrs. Wick. We took them into the drawing-room where the red embers of the fire still glowed. Bunty rekindled it with sticks. John and Mr. Wick walked between the front door and the back, calling to each other to note the flares, the planes and the bumps. Amaryllis put on the kettle and brought in huge cups of tea.

When the attack was over, our neighbours went to their home again. While John was fastening the doors we washed the tea cups and, feeling rather strung up but supremely glad the ordeal had not been longer, we went back to bed

How many of our thoughts flew to those who had been in the thick of it – wherever that might be! Sleep was slow in coming, and then, just as I was really settling down and that pleasant dreamy cessation of consciousness was stealing over me, the banshee-siren began wailing, and the banging, rattling and loud explosions started once more.

We got into our clothes again. It was early in the morning and very cold. John said I had better stay under the bedclothes and keep as warm as possible; there was no need to go downstairs unless he called. I lay with the eiderdown well pulled up, but ready to leap out at any moment, until once more the dreadfulness died away, and sleep, Nature's sweet restorer, nearly found me.

Alas, yet a third time that night the *Luftwaffe* came – came in strength with the pitiless power and vengeance of which we had read, but which we had not experienced before. But even nights of terror pass away at last. At six o'clock we drew back the curtains. Dawn was coming and the birds began to sing.

Amaryllis, when she came downstairs, discovered there was no gas. She induced a kettle to boil on the water-heater. She told us the whole Village had been up all night, and that the main attack had been on the City of the West.

My thoughts naturally flew to my mother's household! After all their escapes and their long sojourn here – had they really, at last, come in for it! The bangs had not seemed to us quite so far away, but sounds at a distance are difficult to judge and we had no authentic information.

Then came a very loud knocking on our front door. John in his dressing-gown answered it. I felt as certain as I could that it was someone with bad news! I heard a man's voice telling something – asking something. John was taking the unknown man into the drawing-room. I distinctly heard the word "casualty". There on the stairs, leaning on the banisters, I began to shake – when John appeared! There had been some bombing over the City of the West, but the three sharp attacks had been upon our Roman City! The unknown man had been sent to ask Bunty to go to St. Quentin's hospital where casualties were being received.

"Oh, dear! and I have given away all my aprons!" That was Bunty's first thought. But in a few minutes she was dashing down to the Cottage Hospital to her friend Rachel, and she came back again with one of Rachel's dresses, a cap and some aprons, and was ready to start at the appointed hour.

I watched her go off, looking so calm and capable, not to a carefully-staged mock affair this time, but to real solemn service for those who were disabled.

Amaryllis and I made up with clean sheets every bed in the house. Telephones and telegrams were reserved for hospitals and the police, but I thought my own people might come before night. Those who have lived through this sort of thing will be aware of the tense feeling of uncertainty which prevails. Life has swung right out of its usual orbit, and anything of any sort may be expected to happen at any moment.

But nothing else happened that day. We managed to prepare meals on the drawing-room fire, and in the evening Bunty came off duty. She did not say much. She had made up beds, she had washed some of the casualties – black dust and bits of shrapnel fell out of their hair. Some were badly hurt. An old man with cut legs gave her an orange. A baby six weeks old and two little boys were at St. Quentin's; no one as yet had claimed them. Of the saddest sights and the most horrible side of the business she told us nothing.

Amaryllis, whose evening out it was, said that all along the road, as her friends motored her home, she saw people with prams and rugs sheltering for the night in the lanes. Their fear was not misplaced. That Sunday night the raiders came again, and again John and I got up. This second attack was worse than the first. The glow in the sky opposite our front door was blood red, like the Northern Lights. Within myself I was truly and thoroughly frightened. That fear-striking drone of heavy planes overhead – all those thunderous bangs and explosions – would they never cease?

Bunty slept the sleep of the utterly weary and we were loath to rouse her, though to me it seemed that at any moment the whole house might come down. But John thought there was no immediate danger and said she should be allowed to sleep on. He kept running outside the front door and saying: "They'll have the whole City down tonight. There'll be no City left!"

Indeed, it seemed that no City built as the Roman City is built could survive such attacks. Set in a basin and surrounded by green hills, she had for long contained so many memoried monuments of the England we love and reverence. Her ancient Abbey, her lordly Circus and her Royal Crescent, her healing springs, her fountains and her gardens – truly these things have made her a Queen among cities, but she was alas! an easy target from the air.

The Village had, naturally, been up all night, and on Monday morning, in the absence of instruction but in the presence of such dire necessity, it was decided to open the Rest Centre, which had been carefully arranged and equipped ready for the catastrophe of invasion.

The National School was the appointed place, and Mrs. Firth and Mrs. Ellison were the ladies in charge. That Monday morning the scholars very gleefully dispersed, and the schoolrooms were cleared for action. A band of helpers assembled. Oil stoves from a consignment sent by the U.S.A. to every hospital in Britain were commandeered. Mr. Hazeldean supplied bread, cooked meats, margarine, buns and cakes. Piles of sandwiches were cut. Milk, mattresses, easy chairs, blankets and rugs were delivered in procession.

A board with the word 'REST' upon it was set up in the school yard, and in the afternoon the victims of the raid began to come in. Two elderly women were the first to arrive. They had walked the whole way – five miles – and were dead beat. They stood at the school-house door asking whether they might come in, and could they be given shelter for the night?

After that there was a rush. By train, bus, on lorries and in vans, refugees came to our Rest Centre. They all carried bundles or baggage of some kind, and all made the same inquiry: might they stay all night? Anywhere just to feel safe – on the floor, in a chair, just a roof over them and to be free from fear.

The forty-eight hours which is the usual limit for keeping Rest Centres open was extended to a week. The helpers laboured in shifts and they were kept hard at it. Practically everyone in the Village lent a hand, and the Belfry Roaders turned up trumps and gave their evenings to the good work.

Workers going back each morning to the Roman City told their intimates of the hospitality to be found in our Village. So each evening the numbers increased, and the affair tended to become quite a happy gathering of fellow townsfolk. There was much chatting, much comparing of notes over the happenings of those two dreadful nights – tales of the dive-bombers like great black eagles swooping low over the streets and machine-gunning casualties as they were being brought out of wrecked buildings.

Sometimes, right in the midst of a white-faced quivering-lipped recital, would come a roar of laughter over some paltry little joke. Then the tension would relax, and the Red Cross nurse in charge for the night would gently suggest that perhaps they might be just a *little* quieter. One would scarcely have thought they could laugh so easily, nor so often, but the situation had its humorous side. The visitors soon appropriated certain corners, spreading out their blankets and arranging their possessions. One old lady carefully removed her shoes, placed her teeth in one and her spectacles in the other, and settled down for a comfortable snooze.

Those who had to leave very early tip-toed between rows of slumbering figures, while every board creaked, and the two doors clanked and clicked in the noisiest manner possible to doors. At half-past six Mrs. Edgelow, from the corner shop, brought over a steaming urn already boiled on her own fire and placed it on the oil stove in the school-room. Cups of tea were soon circulating, and there were some scrambles for the use of the school wash-basins.

Those were chiefly the adults. Mothers with babies were sent to the Wesleyan Chapel along the Tyning, and in this small Bethel the mothers found sanctuary. Mrs. Firth said that she was particularly impressed by their fortitude. One girl had walked in the lanes for two nights carrying her few-weeks'-old baby. But all she said was: "Oh! isn't it nice to sit down?"

Our visitors were not all British. A party of Indians arrived at the chapel. There were twelve of them, including small children and four babies in arms. Bomb and blast had wrecked the flat they had occupied, and so they had walked out along the roads all together. When Mrs. Firth said: "Why didn't you get a lift by the way?" they laughed and said: "Who would stop to pick up twelve?"

When they left, the children brought her hot tight little bunches of dandelions, the flower which most resembled the marigolds with which in their own land they celebrate joyful occasions. All the way along the Tyning they looked back waving their brown hands, and calling out their gratitude.

It is a happy thing for me to tell how our Village opened not only the Rest Centre, but its own kind heart, so that all which was possible was done for these stricken neighbours. In many cottages the householders slept on the floor so that their guests might have the beds. When no more billets could be found, summer-houses, haylofts and barns were pressed into service.

Mrs. Rector brought us our first billetee, Mr. Burke, a small gasping man with a distressing cough. He had managed to get his wife and small children away; he wanted to be no trouble – no trouble at all; just a place to sleep – he must be away early in the morning. No! not even a cup tea – just somewhere to sleep.

We had fixed him up when a messenger from the Rest Centre came to ask whether we could sleep a gentleman who had lost everything. Mr. Wood followed almost at once – middle-aged and harassed, a terribly tired man wearing an old raincoat, but with that subtle something about his speech and manner which demands the prefix "gentle".

John took Mr. Wood in hand, and a little later another knock came. It was another messenger to ask could we take two more persons. I said: "Yes! if they will share a room!"

Shortly afterwards Monsieur and Madame Beck were on the front door step. How can I describe the haggard look of them? John and I met them. We took their hands – or they took ours (I was never quite sure which) – and we led them into our warm room and put them in the comfortable chairs, while in excellent English, and with speaking gestures, they told us how they had spent the last two nights out of doors.

It took a little while to adjust matters upstairs, and Bunty and I were still manipulating bedclothes when a large dairy van rolled up to the door. An anxious-looking man got out. Could we take a lady and her two daughters? I was obliged to tell him that we had no bedroom unoccupied.

He replied: "They have eiderdowns and blankets with them, if you can only give them shelter."

Out from the van stepped a dimpled, fair-haired lady and two girls. They all came in as bright as buttons; it was hard to believe they had lost their all. They had been driving up and down and could not find anyone to take them in. A gentleman out in the road had advised them to come here. We offered them the use of our dining-room. There, with cushions and all the rugs we could assemble, they settled in, and for that night at least our excitements were at as end.

The days which followed were strange and strenuous. The absence of gas made the wheels of the house run heavily. We were glad now of our old black iron kettles, which could be boiled on an open fire without coming to utter destruction. But oh! what a labour it was to get the most simple meal – how grimed our bright saucepans became! How smoke-flavoured tasted our tea and our porridge!

Our guests returned from the Roman City each evening between eight and nine o'clock, and over a hob fixed on the drawing-room fire we made coffee while we heard their items of news. The City was being cleaned up, but the general devastation was depressing. Our British-Belgian friends had already had much experience of raids. Because he was British-born and had a son in the R.A.F., they left Brussels two days before the Germans entered it. Bombed and machine-gunned at Ostend, they had an adventurous passage to Dover, and they were also in the worst of the London blitzes.

Mr. Wood had been joined by his wife, and they visited the heap of rubble which had been their home for twenty-five years. They found a bunch of keys and an overcoat, and a few oddments beside. They had to plough through the business of getting clothing coupons and emergency cards. They were continually having to purchase the small amenities we all accumulate at home without knowing we are doing so. But how cheerful they were; how thankful for lives spared, for the sympathy of friends and of strangers.

Mr. Burke – the small man with the bronchial cough – was getting his roof repaired. It was three weeks before he could send for his wife and children, and every night when he had climbed our steep hill he expressed wheezily, and with difficulty, his pleasure in being where it was so quiet and so beautiful.

The nightingales sang, and the apple trees flowered, till like an evil dream the stress and terror of those happenings began to pass away – though not their purifying influence. How could we forget those other lives whose earthly witness was so suddenly cut short? Or put away from our memories the bereaved and stricken families whose dear ones were missing?

Why was it allowed to happen?

There were some who asked that! And they were chiefly those who had borne with equanimity the bombing of Warsaw and Rotterdam.

It was not easy to answer them – not easy to explain that man had willed to be free from God. This war and all it calamities was the fruit, and not the root of the trouble.

# STONES OF BRITAIN

Quarried so patiently –
Hammered and chiselled –
Builded to beauty
   Of cornice and crown;
Stones which our forefathers
Wrought into majesty
All in a moment
   Of madness thrown down.

Market place! Music place!
Homing place! Worship place!
Flung into fragments
   With thunderous power;
Places our forefathers
Frequented lovingly;
Treasures they kept for us
   Gone in an hour.

What shall we say of them?
Stones of old Coventry,
York stones and Bristol stones,
   Shattered away.
Bath stones and Norwich stones,
Stones of old London.
Citizens! Citizens!
   What shall we say?

Fire cannot filch from us
Memory's storing house;
Bombs cannot blast from us
   Days we have known.
Music which nobled us,
Worship which moulded us –
Citizens ! Citizens!
   These are our own.

*Chapter Fourteen*

## THE CHANGES WHICH ARE SURE TO COME

THE GREAT UPHEAVAL BEING OVER, THAT SMALL SELFISH heart of mine began to think it would be nice to slip back to our ordinary ways. Those little nests which we are careful to build around our lives are too snug, and too comfortable, for us to like being turned out of them for long. To work at one's own work again, one's home for just the family circle again – those are the longings which hover around us after we have been pushed, and shaken, and terribly fluttered.

After nearly a fortnight, during which we all rode upon the crest of a tidal wave of high endeavour, things began to slow down. Amaryllis was in good spirits. She announced that if she could but get hold of Hitler, she would put him to stand at the sink and clean our smoke-blackened saucepans. She would make him wash the extra teacloths we were using; he should darn the holes in the Turkish towels which our refugee men-folk managed to cut in wiping their razors.

M. and Madame Beck, our Belgian-British friends, had left us. Mr. Wood had taken rooms in the Village for himself and his wife, and would go to them at the end of the week. Mr. Burke's roof was now repaired, he was taking possession of his house again on the morrow, and with these releases in prospect I began to plan once more to build around my old foundations.

I had an unfinished article to touch up, and I had just received suggestions from my publisher about a new book. Therefore, how glad I should be when I could again leave cooking, bed-making and washing-up to Amaryllis.

John had his own special work of organization always pulling at him – close, careful work which has up to the present kept us from being "on the phone", so that he may when in his own home get a modicum of peace. Bunty was going to make a dead set at preparations for her nursing career, and as we three sat together at our early supper, we were each of us glad to think the "run" was nearly over, and that we could get down to work again.

We did not know – for how seldom we ever do know – that life for us had already taken a swing right away from the old familiar days. Not yet – if ever – were we to go back to being that little circle of "just ourselves". A ring came at the back door.

Bunty answered it. It was only a note for Mr. Wood. But a few minutes later John looked up from his supper and saw two strangers, a lady and gentleman, approaching the front door.

They had heard of us from M. and Madame Beck and had come to ask whether we could let them have sleeping accommodation for a week. They had been through a bad time and had had little rest. He was engaged all day in important work. She was in charge of a canteen. They would bring an electric ring, get their own supper and early tea, and be away again before we were up. What could we do but say they could come?

They had not been gone many minutes when, while crossing the hall, I saw a nice-looking and well-groomed young man standing at the door. He said that he had come from the Office of Works and Buildings and would like to see the house.

My heart made a sudden leap upwards into my throat! See the house! *Our* house! I knew only too well what that might mean. The big houses around had nearly all been visited, and the occupants told to hold themselves in readiness to quit, as the place they called their home might be requisitioned for Government purposes at any time.

Ours is not a big house. It is a moderate house set in a large garden. The good-looking and courteous young man, after seeing and measuring the rooms, said: "I suppose you don't want to leave?"

We said we didn't!

Then he said: "I suppose you have nowhere to go?"

We said we hadn't!

The young man then admitted that the premises were not nearly as large as they anticipated, and he thought it was not very likely that they would disturb us – though, of course, one never knew what might happen!

But that remark, I reflected, was, perhaps, made as a temporary comfort. Probably he glimpsed the horror and dismay which rushed in on me like a tide. He departed, and John, Bunty and I looked at each other. So that might be the next thing! We, too, might find ourselves homeless. We, too, might lose so much that was dear and familiar. I said: "Whatever shall we do if they take it?"

John said: "It will be no worse for us than for anyone else." This was unanswerable though – like Mrs. Gummidge – I would like to have said: *I feels it more.*

Mr. Wood came home and read the letter which was on the hall table. It was from his prospective landlady – she regretted she was unable to give Mr. and Mrs. Wood accommodation, and hoped they would soon find something to suit them. Dreadfully "down" as I felt myself, Mr. Wood was even more disconsolate.

He knew as well as we did that every hole and corner in the Village had been "taken". People were still sleeping in summer-houses, in haylofts and barns, and even out in tents. He had no hope of finding anything and his disappointment was profound.

"I want somewhere," he said, "to sit and talk things over with my wife, and decide what we had better do. I want a little time to get my bearings again. My wife will be here to-morrow. It's too late to wire her not to come."

Naturally, John told him to let his wife come here for a few days while they looked round. "One more," said John, "won't make much difference and, perhaps, she will lend a hand."

Mrs. Wood came, and the hand she lent was so capable we began to wonder how we had managed without it.

As we swept and dusted the bedrooms, Mrs. Wood told me a little more concerning the actual experience of an air-raid. They were a household of five, her mother, sister and a billetee were living with them. It was about eleven o'clock on Saturday night – they were all upstairs in bed except Mr. Wood who was still reading by the fire.

Planes began to go over, but Mrs. Wood took little notice because this was so usual. Then there was an alert. Mr. Wood shouted up the stairs for them to come down, and as they came the bombs began to drop. The three women had just got into the small shelter under the stairs when the house was hit.

Stones and masonry fell on Mr. Wood pinning his legs. With an effort he wriggled himself free. He could see the sky through the roof. He could hear wardens shouting: "Is anyone there?" Then rescuers came in and removed debris from the door of the shelter. The billetee was badly injured and was taken to hospital. The others were led and carried out through the window, down the back garden, and into a public shelter across the road.

Mrs. Wood had snatched up a rug and a long coat – this was all they had to put on over their night attire, and the night was cold. The screaming of the bombs, Mrs. Wood said, was more terrifying than the noise when they dropped. More than once that crowded shelter rocked from end to end – more than once they thought their last moment had arrived – yet no one cried out.

No one was hysterical; she was not even sure whether they actually prayed; they just stuck it, all through those three deadly attacks, and when at last the raid was over, by great good fortune Mr. Wood got a taxi, and they went to some special friends whose house had not suffered and who gladly took them in.

On Sunday they visited their own house. The front door had slipped right down – but they were able to get in through a back window, and very precariously managed to rescue several of her mother's things and a few of their own. Being utterly weary and the cold so intense, they decided to leave any further salvage till Monday morning. But after the second raid on Sunday night the rest of the house had disappeared. There was literally nothing left but a heap of rubble with an old tablecloth on the top.

On Monday they left the city. Trains were so crowded, and so late, they could not get away till evening, and it was nearly midnight when, wearing borrowed clothes and feeling, Mrs. Wood said, dirty and unkempt in the extreme, they arrived in

Sarum and went to a hotel. A few days later she took her mother and sister to friends, and in the meantime Mr. Wood had found sanctuary here.

"And now," she added, with her countenance so calmly cheerful no one would have guessed at her losses, "I am here too, waiting for the next move."

A few days, later Amaryllis told me she had decided to "go in for war work", and that she would be leaving as soon as I could release her.

I think I knew then that the "changes which are sure to come" had come to us for the duration! I knew that I should miss Amaryllis for she was the sort of "stand by" who would get through things whatever went wrong.

Every night I discussed the next day's meals with her, but I always found she had already planned them, and she just told me what she had decreed we should have. She was an early riser, and she never forgot the black-out. Yes, I should miss her, because she carried quite a good deal of the load, and though it is pleasant to have the run of your own kitchen, it is also pleasant to feel free from the duties which follow each other so rapidly in every household worthy of the name of home.

However, "in acceptance lieth peace". Our present circumstances were Hobson's choice – we could not alter them. Yet, as John said, "there is all the difference in the world between accepting them and kicking furiously at them."

After some worried moments on my part, and more than one unrestful night, there was a lessening of the strain. Scent of wallflowers came in at the doors and windows and our wisteria, so long reluctant and shy of showing bloom, this year did herself proud. Over the wall by the back door, round the corner to Bunty's bedroom window, the pale mauve fingers spread in perfect cascades of blossom. And suddenly, without notice, on a Tuesday evening *the gas came back*.

This may seem a little thing and scarcely worth recording, but the difference it made was amazing. I had never given thanks for gas before! I had just taken for granted that pipes were laid on, and that by paying a bill once a quarter one could get so many facilities for cooking and heating, with such a small expenditure of toil.

In spite of the fireplace in the sitting-room, and in spite of the electric ring lent to us by our "lodgers", even boiling a kettle or warming a little milk had become feats of cleverness and ingenuity. The return of the gas cheered us all. Amaryllis made scones and a rhubarb pie and, when she was leaving, offered to come in every evening to get our supper. This offer I was only too glad to accept.

Our household now comprised Mr. and Mrs. Wood and our three selves – though Bunty would soon be leaving to begin her training in the City of the West. We held a conference and discussed what we had better do. Two courses were open to us. We could all go to hotels, or stay on and try to run this house on the simplest possible lines. Eventually this is what we decided to do. Home life means a good deal to persons like us, and the Woods were like-minded. We decided that, anyway, we would resolutely cut out all frills, and with our two men-folk away all day, it should not be very difficult just to keep the house going.

In the middle of June Bunty, with her neat outfit of caps, aprons and starched frocks, departed to begin being a nurse in real earnest. She went first to the Preliminary Training School for the usual two months' course. We had read, and we had heard, so much about the hardships of a nurse's life that it was pleasant to discover that this first part of the programme, at any rate, proved to be a happy experience. A dozen girls of varying ages and dispositions, in charge of a live and humorous Sister, can have very good times indeed. They rose early, and some of them got the breakfast, while others polished floors and otherwise cleaned the house. They washed up, and were ready to attend lectures by ten o'clock. The School was a tall old house up numerous steps, and Bunty (having long arms) was deputed to lean out, and sweep the dust and leaves from the area entrance. She thoroughly enjoyed everything, and came home on Saturdays full of enthusiasm for her new venture.

Our national affairs were not so rosy. In North Africa our troops were forced to retreat before Rommel, and while Mr. Churchill was in Washington came the culminating disaster of the loss of Tobruk. Times seemed very dark again. Hong Kong forced to surrender; Singapore, where 70,000 Imperial troops laid down their arms – and now Tobruk! Our few successes seemed to melt away into insignificance. Why was it that, for so long, all we put our hands to seemed to elude and to go against us? The angry debate and vote of censure on the central direction of the war, which took place in the House of Commons, grieved some of us to the heart.

There was no serious mistake in the central direction of the war. Our own past apathy and unpreparedness were the faults which had brought about our reverses. Sudden patriotism and feverish declamations could not atone for that, nor keep back the inevitable harvest of our careless years. Mr. Churchill left his critics without a word to say, and the vote of confidence he subsequently received must have cheered his spirit.

In our Village things had in a manner settled down again, though there was a distinct difference. Practically every house was again entertaining strangers. The raids on the Roman City, and the contacts of the Rest Centre had re-opened the whole question of billeting, and Mrs. Wills was busier than ever. Many amusing and some touching incidents were the outcome of that sudden trek from the City. People whose homes had suffered no injury did not want to go back, and a certain Mrs. Tripp with a hook nose, and a very determined jaw, refused to leave the Village. Her hostess, an old lady who took in washing, came to Mrs. Wills in real distress.

"If you please, Mam, would you tell her to go, for I can't. Because when I do, she says she is a poor widow, and being a widow myself, I know what it is. But I can't keep her, for my washing has got all behind owing to her talking so much, and my customers keeps on calling to know if it's ready. And if you please, Mam, after I'd had her a week she went away and brought back a dog as well. And my cat can't abide dogs – so, please, do come down and tell her she must go back home."

There was also the case of the sick old man who carried all his possessions in a small cardboard box. He had lived over an old clothes shop which was entirely demolished, and now he had nowhere to go. When the Rest Centre closed, Mrs. Wills was obliged to send him back to the City Authorities, who would find him a place where he could be housed and tended.

Our home affairs ran smoothly enough, but the housework was becoming rather much, when added to the continuous fruit gathering and jam making. Amaryllis had left the district, and we tried in vain to get a "woman" to come in and do a little cleaning. I still had commissioned work on hand. And, presently, John said in that determined way of his that he would "have no more of it". He put an advertisement in the local press offering living accommodation in return for help with household duties.

The times being what they were, we had many and diverse applications. John's advice was "see them all!" So having picked out the three most likely applicants, Mrs. Wood and I went to interview them. Mr. Bagshaw drove us. The addresses given were not easy to find, and were a considerable distance apart.

Alas! when at last we had run all three to earth not one of them was suitable. In short, the applicants wanted accommodation, but they did not want the accompanying household duties. There was the lady who went to some pains to tell us she had always kept a maid and a charwoman. The lady who was prepared to do a little gardening if that would help, and also the lady who had applied for our post without telling her husband, and he refused to let her consider it!

Somewhat disappointed, and dismayed, we went on steadily through the increasing number of applicants, for the advertisement appeared every day for a week, and eventually we interviewed Mr. and Mrs. Gray.

As soon as we saw them I think we knew that our search was over. Their home in the City had been destroyed, and with their son, Edmund, they were living in an army hut, which was pleasant in summer, but would be very inconvenient in cold weather. Mrs. Gray was prepared to help in any way she could; her husband and son would be away all day, and she would have plenty of time. They saw our rooms and were pleased with them. The little kitchenette, the separate staircase, and the pleasant sitting-room all gave satisfaction. It was more than agreeable to us to find that what we had to offer was evidently so acceptable to them.

The Grays came, and with their coming the household entered once more upon a new and hitherto untried experience. Strange people living in our house! How we had always dreaded it, and had said we would rather live in two rooms.

I had been quite certain that they would create the two things I most hate – smells and noises; that they would bang doors, cook bloaters or cabbage at all hours, and have the wireless on without ceasing. The Grays proved to be the quietest, cleanest, and most considerate of tenants. The father and son reminded us of Miss Matty's eulogy concerning her maid's husband, Jim, who was a very pleasant man to have in the house, for she never saw him from week's end to week's end.

All this time Russia was miraculously holding on. Hitler was still holding forth, Japan was still making headway and threatening Australia and India, and also, all this time, silently and secretly, the embarkation of our troops went on.

From wayside stations dim with the dusk of evening, with drawn blinds, and the rumble-rumble of the train in their ears, our lads were leaving behind the things they knew, and going out into the unknown. Passing English farms, English fields, English rivers, English towns, till at last in an English dawnlight they stood waiting upon a English quay. And as their ship set sail; they sang.

# THERE IS MUCH TO LOVE IN ENGLAND

There is so much to love in England
For those who are English bred:
So much to love and cherish in our England:
Such hallowed ground to tread!
So much to look for, and to love, in England –
The flowering thorn –
Young emerald corn –
Rivers upflashing on an April morn –
And the lovely English land outspread.

There is so much to love in England:
The furrowed men who toil –
The gallant, gay, young fighting men of England –
That strong and stubborn fighter Mr. England
With his plain speech blunt and loyal –
The shiny coated cattle bred in England –
Brown ducks with waddling prance –
And leggy lambs that dance –
And children of the stock of England
Playing on the English soil.

And England's sons, exiled and far from England –
Called and enthralled thereby –
Salt their long, dusty days with dreams of England –
England for whom they die!
Her green grass –
Her grey rain –
Her rooks building again –
Her larks still singing over Salisbury Plain –
And some small village church – the faith of England –
Standing foursquare to the sky.

## Chapter Fifteen

### A DREADED VISITATION

BUNTY WITH HER COMRADES-IN-APRONS HAD NEARLY completed an eight weeks' course at the Preliminary School when she brought home with her for the week-end – Sally!

Sally hailed from the Channel Islands. She had left her home just before the German occupation. She had had no news of her parents except a brief message through the Red Cross.

I liked Sally. She was dark-haired and shining-eyed, not very tall, though strength and endurance showed itself in her build. Beside her, Bunty looked rather like a lamppost, but they got on together amazingly, and they made an earnest request: might they have the use of the kitchen that evening to practise Invalid Cookery for their impending exam? Bunty added that the things they made would do for our suppers.

They gave us soup, steamed fish, and vanilla custard, and though they could not be said to possess "invalid" appetites themselves, their efforts made a nice addition to our Saturday night supper, which in these days was chiefly salad and cheese, with cooked American bacon when we could get it. The food situation, while not easy, might have been very much worse.

Although we live close to a farm, the milk ration had to be rigidly observed and we learned to get the utmost value out of it. Mr. Edbrooke's cows give the sort of milk which comes up into a thick yellow blob on the top of the bottle, and therefore goes further than the thin blue variety.

Indeed, our Village is quite rightly notorious for its good milk. This is because our hills and valleys are almost entirely grass land. Water springs run among the hills, and in the valley there are always the two rivers, suiting each other like married partners – one so leisurely and slow and silent, and the other as quick and jubilant and talkative as ever a river could be.

Naturally, our neighbourhood is rich in dairy farms. They all have Englishy names – Home Farm, Pond House Farm, Fairclose, Uplands, Hillside, Pipards Farm.

One thing the timorous visitor to our district finds trying – you cannot cross a field without meeting cows! You cannot even run for the early train without finding cows blocking up the narrow, winding lane to the railway station. If you drive a car, you are suddenly confronted by cows coming out of open gateways; cows grazing by the roadside, cows drinking at a wayside pool.

But all our cows, and especially Miss Moxam's, are gentle and almost human creatures. Being our only farmeress, Miss Moxam has a special claim upon the interest of the Village.

It is said that she washes and even combs her cows, and, certainly she calls them by romantic and endearing names. In Miss Moxam, I fancy we enshrine something elemental which, perhaps, I may call "love of the land" – something which is not just a product of the war, for it existed long before the land girl came into being.

Most of us cannot go walking through dripping fields at daybreak, we cannot milk cows, nor can we keep pigs – but we like to see Miss Moxam doing it. At haymaking time everybody who can lends Miss Moxam a hand. Everybody helps her to haul swedes and mangolds. I am sure that in helping Miss Moxam we are subconsciously giving something to ourselves – to that half-hidden, subtle self which loves the good earth, and has some kinship with all that is in it.

Bunty, having safely and creditably negotiated the examination, began her experience as a "pro" in a city hospital. She was given a tin hat, a bunch of keys, and a bedroom to herself. In the latter she found plenty of drawers and cupboards, a long mirror, a bookcase and two chairs. The furniture looked rather kicked about, but the bed was comfortable.

In hospital life there are, of course, rules and regulations, but, quite frankly, I am of the opinion that these "restrictions" do not unduly restrict those who have never habitually kept late hours, nor asked unusual concessions from life.

With regard to the pay for pros, and for nurses in general, I do not think it is exactly lavish! But any girl who chooses nursing as a profession is sure of a certain standard of living; a room to herself; plenty of hot baths, even though only five inches of water is allowed; and definite off-times. Above all, she has an opportunity of touching, and helping in her everyday life, that ever-recurring, age-old problem – the problem of suffering. Highly-paid, unskilled and arbitrary workers may draw the money, but nurses draw upon surpassingly rich material which money cannot buy.

Much has been said about the poor food in hospital, but Bunty, who is particular – not to say finicky – has found it good in quality and nicely cooked. All the same, the first time she came home she said: "It is rather nice to sit down to a properly-laid table. In hospital we go in through the kitchen, collect a plateful, dump it down somewhere at a table, and eat."

After a few months John and I observed that she was losing the lamp-posty look; her face had rounded out, and in spite of there being "no second helpings" Bunty was putting on weight! In her ward she was, of course, a very little person, just wiping lockers, making beds, helping with meals, and performing the most humble ministries. She found her superiors considerate and helpful, and the patients all "very nice". Most of them were, apparently, surprised by the atmosphere of friendly cheerfulness. One patient said: "I didn't know hospital would be like this!"

The war situation at this time was exceedingly serious. The Russians were hard pressed in the Caucasus when news came that Gandhi and the Congress Party were on the point of revolt against British rule, and about to negotiate with Japan. It was also rumoured that the Japanese were planning to attack Russia.

To those of us who knew only what the newspapers told us,

it seemed strange that the United Nations were so quiet. Even sensible people asked each other when we were going to open that Second Front? And, of course, that section of the public which loves a grievance set on foot an agitation intending to prod our leaders into action.

*Open a Second Front Now* was chalked upon pavements, and upon the walls of public buildings. It also made a good slogan for heckling Ministers of the Crown at public meetings. But our Supreme War Council was not to be stampeded into anything. Like Brer Rabbit it "went on saying nuffin", and except for bombing ports and industrial targets on the Continent, the men of the forces appeared to be still waiting.

But while we were questioning, and even getting impatient, our Mr. Churchill had gone secretly to Russia, via the Middle East, and was having conferences with M. Stalin. "He was there," said the Know-alls when the news came through, "to find out when, and where, we had better open a Second Front."

Two days after our Prime Minister returned from Russia a most sudden and saddening calamity befell our Royal Family. The Duke of Kent was killed in an air crash.

These woeful tidings sent a pang of grief through the Village. We are loyal folk with a personal affection and admiration for our Royal House. At the time of the Silver Jubilee only one house in the Village omitted to put out flags. We were deeply hurt, especially when the head of that house said: "It is time we had done with kings!"

Our King to us is not just the head of the State. He is our representative man. Our King and Queen and their children are our representative family; how they behave, and how they think about things, matters tremendously to England and the Empire. They are bound up with us, and we are bound up with them. When we suffer from fire, mining disasters, floods or bombing, they are on the spot directly to sympathize with us.

And we English people with our English eyes follow intently all that happens to our Royal House. We have gone all the way with them on their crowning days, their jubilees, their weddings; and in their days of sorrow it is our desire to go with them all the way too. Now, more than ever, because of the troublous times and the general uncertainty of life, our hearts were sore for them when death suddenly struck down this handsome and gallant prince.

Though our Village is such a small community it has been our pride to think of ourselves as open-minded. We like to remember that even an inland village can receive the wash of tides from far-away shores. We have even learned to talk glibly of cities and of localities which once we scarcely knew were on the map, because the lovers, husbands and sons of the Village are marching over desert sands, sailing upon perilous seas, or hurtling air-borne through the skies.

Until, all at once, our eyes which were becoming long-sighted were turned inwards, and for long, long weeks were focused upon ourselves – upon our farms and our farmers, and upon the live creatures to which they gave shelter and care. Summer with all its enchantment had brought to our county a great menace. Cases of foot-and-mouth disease were being reported.

The news was received with the utmost dismay. Twenty-five years had passed since a similar visitation came upon the Village. The memory of it was recalled with horror. Even Mr. Piggott's cheerfully rubicund countenance became grave as he spoke of it.

It was talked of anxiously not only in farmyards and milking sheds but in Mr. Hazeldean's shop, over garden walls, and at the Inn. There was nothing at all like panic, but it seemed as though a dark cloud suddenly overshadowed and might at any moment burst upon us.

It was true that just then the cattle in the Village were in good health, feeding well and looking well, but as this evil thing came nearer and nearer the farmers, so Mr. Edbrooke expressed it, became very suspicious and all of a tremor. When it broke out in the village next to ours, they were afraid of seeing anyone coming from that village lest they should have brought the infection.

From first thing in the morning till last thing at night the men of the fields were watching the cows, as the terrible scourge crept nearer. It reached one of the hillsides opposite our own hills. How real, how ever-present, was the dread of it! How powerless it seemed was all human skill to circumvent it! Had these been the days of witchcraft, that starkly evil thing would have been visualized as a sinister presence stalking slowly towards us.

One evening, coming up from the station, Mrs. Wood saw a

group of men, among whom were two police officers, in the field which skirts the roadway. She heard someone say: "Abingdons have got it."

The Abingdons' fields run along by the river towards Broadwater. One cow was a little lame; the County Vet, passing by after visiting an infected farm, had noticed it and had made the dreaded pronouncement.

So, it had come! This long feared and deadly danger was actually present with us. The shock and sorrow which this brought to the Abingdon household cannot be described. We all grieved that they should have to face this tragic thing. Not only the infected animal, but the whole herd had to be slaughtered, and every precaution taken to prevent the disease spreading.

Now, indeed, the other farmers lived from hour to hour "all in a tremor", watching their cattle anxiously and dreading what they might see. Cows could not now be moved from the field where they happened to be, and this alone made the creatures dissatisfied and uneasy. Change from one field to another is essential for their well-being, and though they were given hay, they had no taste for it at this time of the year. They were continually breaking out, through hedges and other boundaries, in search of fresh pasture.

Miss Moxam's milking yard is separated from the Abingdons' by a wall. Everard Abingdon called to her to tell her his distressful news. She immediately drove her cows through the river (they were not allowed on the road) and under Leland's bridge into the field called Cleves.

Cleves is a long field which widens at the gateway end and then runs narrowly beside the river, making a green roadway bordered by hawthorn hedges. Here in the spring the blackcaps sing, and here dippers haunt the flat stones over which the water swirls and chatters. The cows were used to Cleves, the grass there is specially sweet – sweeter even than the grass in Little Mead. With camphor balls round their necks they fed contentedly, and Miss Moxam milked them there.

At six o'clock in the morning the whole herd was happy and well-liking; at one o'clock Bella was observed to be bubbling at the mouth. Miss Moxam telephoned the Police. They, with the County Vet, were on the spot directly, and the dreaded formalities went forward.

The Valuer began his round and Miss Moxam had to accompany him. But how could one "value", in coin of the realm, that which was invaluable? Daisy – half-Guernsey and half-Shorthorn, the loveliest cow in the world. Priscilla – fat and lazy, who during milking always put her nose on the trough and went to sleep and snored. Bella – the heifer bought at Chippenham market. The weaning calf – a red roan who pushed her friendly nose into the bucket, and whose name was – *Malta!*

Cynthia, Laura, Rosebud, Cherry – the Valuer stood beside each, estimated and made notes. That same night they were all slaughtered. Then followed the excavator to dig the pits. There, beside the river, the gentle-eyed creatures were laid that the grass might grow above them, and the evil thing be purged away.

These bare facts set down in cold print give no idea of what all this meant to those of us who were so close to it. Folk who live in near touch with the land are not given to making glib and gushing speeches. Like the ploughshare, cutting into their own brown earth, this thing ploughed deeply beneath the surface.

On successive days we heard that "it" had come to Uplands, to Pond House Farm, to Pipards. The smell of disinfectant filled the air. A police officer stood at the entrance of every infected farm. Field paths were closed. Pasted on stiles and fastened to gates were notices printed in red:

*This path is Closed! Foot-and-Mouth Disease.*

Dogs had to be kept tethered, and could only be taken out on leads. Dog owners found themselves in for an anxious time, but they were not half so anxious as were the farmers whose cows were still in health.

Then one morning Michael brought the news that Edbrookes had got it. Edbrookes is our next-door farm, the farm which has supplied us with milk and eggs ever since we have been living in the Village. Edbrookes' cows pasture chiefly in the green water meadows which we see from our windows. We are accustomed, every morning before we are up, to hear Edbrookes' cows lumbering along the lane at the bottom of our garden.

Hillman, who helps Mr. Edbrooke, is a singing man, and he sings to that gentle lumber-lumber. The cows go up, along, and around the most dangerous corner which ever curved itself into the middle of four roads. They push into the milking yard, and after that they are turned into the hilly meadow known as The Gallery, where the row of walnut trees stands overlooking the Tyning.

As the cows came in one morning, Mr. Edbrooke noticed that Buttercup was a little lame. How quickly the rest followed! The Police, the Vet, the Valuer, all filling up the milking yard and handing Mr. Edbrooke papers to sign, till this quiet, unhurried man of the fields said protestingly: "Well, if I'd committed a crime you couldn't be making more of a to-do than you are now."

The police advised that the butchers should be sent for forthwith.

"They came in," said Mr. Edbrooke, "shouting and talking very loud. The cattle were all in the shed, and when they heard the strange voices they began to jump, and to tremble all over.

"Hillman, he went to the butchers – his face was white as could be – and he said, 'Look here,' he said, 'these cows have never been shouted at, nor hammered about. *I'll* come in, and tie the halters on them.' And that," said Mr. Edbrooke, "broke me down."

One thing impressed itself upon those who gave any careful thought to this visitation – the fortitude of the farmers. It means much to get a herd of cows together. They are not purchased at market in the mass, but selected one at time for their separate milking qualities. The loss of them was not merely the loss of possessions, for compensation was made. It was the personal side which grieved and sank deeply in. Those whose work it is to tend and care for any members of the dumb creation know well what intensely intimate work it is. There is a contact, indescribable in words, which exists between the tended and the one who tends.

In various ways – individual as well as collective – they know and they trust the hand which unfailingly brings food, opens gates, guides to pastures, and to water. Miss Moxam expressed the uppermost thought in the minds of such when she said: "I can't bear for them to think I've let them down."

I think, too, that Farmer Jeffery put into words his own

feelings, and those of his fellows, when he said:

"At first – for the first few hours after I knew – it seemed as though I could not bear it. It seemed more than could be borne. But afterwards I thought: Well – it has happened – and I shall have to face it. And I found that I could!"

This was the voice of England in our Village – the authentic voice of England!

# A LITANY FOR CATTLE MEN

I think a litany might well be written
  Solely for cattle men,
Who serve and sweat, heat burdened, or frost bitten,
  In field and cattle pen.

Some patient priest – a countryman – should write it,
  A man of sun and snows;
He could frame such a litany and light it
  With the grand truths he knows.

A litany with simple Saxon phrases
  Which simple folk could say,
Handling cold turnips on a winter morning,
  Or cutting swathes of hay.

For men who meet and brave the winds of heaven
  Seven days in every week,
Some words of thankfulness for courage given
  Should not be far to seek.

Of the bewildered minds of ailing cattle
  No one knows very much
But in this litany there would be, surely,
  A little prayer for such.

For men of English fields and English manners,
  Toiling through nights and days,
In our own English tongue let there be written
  A litany of praise.

# ENGLAND'S SON

*August 26th, 1942*

Who is this comes homing – homing –
Through the shades of August gloaming,
Now the moor puts on her purple
And the night her purple pall?
A king's son
And England's son,
England's son comes homing.

Is this he who went forth lately
With a princely step and stately?
Blithe he went at England's bidding
Who so silent cometh home.
A king's son
And England's son,
England's son comes homing.

This is he! Let England mourn him!
England – whose behest has borne him
To the bounds beyond his journey
Further than the Empire knows.
A king's son
And England's son,
England's son comes homing.

## Chapter Sixteen

### THIS IS MY VILLAGE

FOR A FEW DAYS WE HAD NO MILK. MR. HAZELDEAN'S shop was besieged, and he obliged as many customers as possible with the tinned variety. Those who could not get any borrowed or begged from their neighbours. Then a notice was put in Mrs. Edgelow's shop window, and a messenger went round the Village to say that those who brought receptacles could obtain milk by going to the School House corner at three o'clock.

Mrs. Wood and I went down at the appointed time, and I have seldom seen the Village so well represented. Mrs. Wendover, stout and comfortable, with a jug and a milk-can, was leaning over the school wall. Dogs on leads stood beside their owners, panting and straining to be free. Children swarmed in and out of Mrs. Edgelow's, depositing their jugs on the step, and taking the extreme risk of kicking them to smithereens as they came out. High and low, frigid, friendly, native, refugee, all met on equal terms that day at the School corner. Little, lady-like afternoon tea-jugs hobnobbed with common hardware.

At last the dairy van came rumbling down the road so rapidly it is a wonder it did not land itself in the deep ditch, where water forget-me-nots grow and wagtails wade. The van swirled, round the corner and drew up. We all crowded to the pavement, and now began the procession of mugs, jugs, bottles, cans and even saucepans. The good-natured men in charge of the van filled them all. The smallest children stood drinking large sips of milk and presently we all dispersed, carrying our treasure carefully not to spill a drop – and the van went on its beneficent way to supply other milkless areas.

About this time the King appointed Thursday, the third of September, as a day of prayer. It is true that during our recent season of testing, prayer was offered in our church and in our chapel, asking strength for the farmers and for faith to accept this time of adversity without bitterness. It is true that day by day a small loyal band of praying folk still met for intercession for our land, our lads, and for our Allies. But now when, by the King's command, we went after three years of war to the old grey church, we went with a new awareness.

The shallow steps at the church door were worn towards the middle by the passage of countless feet. The church itself seemed dark and solemn as we went in. Soft music was coming from the organ. Miss Merrill was playing, for Walt, our organist, had been called up.

Sitting under the shadow of the old gallery and organ loft, it seemed to me that history itself was being written. Not new history – the days of old were only repeating themselves. Men, women and children were coming in, just as their forbears had come, sitting in the old, old pews; the same sun falling on the high and ancient window, on the Saxon archway, on the oaken door.

Ours is an ancient parish. Our Village has a background of over a thousand years, and it must have felt the impact of many wars: Alfred with the Danes; the long conflict between Saxon nobles and Norman barons; the Wars of the Roses; assaults of Charles' Royalists and Cromwell's Roundheads; the insurrection led by Monmouth – all these, and other clashes had driven those who came before us to come together to pray for England.

The tablets in our church record honoured names of many who long before the present conflict fought and died for the country of their birth: *Fell in the Punjab – killed in the East Indies – died at Amara from wounds – from enteric fever at Malta.* These words, and others like them, were graven on the neat marble memorials around the walls. Those names reminded us that our England, like that perfect knight King Arthur, was "not intended for private happiness, but for royal joys and the fortunes of a nation".

National affairs were – humanly speaking – very gloomy. Sebastopol had passed into enemy hands. The long, murderous siege of Stalingrad had begun. The Japanese had landed in New Guinea, wholesale massacres of Jews were taking place in the occupied countries.

Prayer is not magic. I do not think that any one amongst us prayed for a sudden spectacular deliverance from all our troubles. But at the end of the day, after the services held all over the country, came the broadcast service which seemed to put its seal upon all. It was not a small thing that with her leaders and statesmen, and her King, our England had once more committed her cause to Almighty God.

Germany with all her vaunted Kultur has no such leadership, for she has put in concentration camps, or otherwise deposed, those who dared to put God before the Führer. For Germany there must be a dark and ominous future – after sowing there comes a reaping time.

It was now that Stalingrad from day to day appeared to be all but taken, yet remained in Russian hands. The defenders were fighting from street to street, and from house to house. It seemed nothing less than a miracle that they could still hold out.

Our malcontents clamoured for more help for Russia. Articles of great bitterness appeared in the press. Reproach was heaped upon our statesmen; and then General Smuts arrived in England. His coming cheered us, and he spoke brave words of counsel and of good hope to both Houses of Parliament. He gave more than a hint of great events impending, but still we waited for such events to arrive.

When they did actually arrive, we were almost staggered by their magnitude. The Russians made their counter offensive. An Allied attack was launched against Axis positions in the Western Desert, and Rommel's Afrika Korps were in full retreat.

We heard this one Thursday morning. The next Sunday John came tearing up the stairs to open my bedroom door that I might hear the news: *American Troops land in French North Africa.*

The thrill which went through the Village was electric. After our long waiting, our many disappointments, and our apparent impotence, it was grand to know that at last a blow had been struck from our side. A good, trouncing, staggering blow which might well be a precursor of the knock-out. The Americans were now attacking the Japanese, the retreating Afrika Korps – pursued by the Eighth Army – was still on the run, and Tobruk was in our hands again. There was, indeed, cause for rejoicing, and it was announced that all over England, on the following Sunday, church bells would be rung to show thanksgiving for victory over Rommel's forces.

Our Doctor had been the captain of our team of ringers. Hitherto we had looked to him to assemble the ringers and to lead them. He it was who, at the Silver Jubilee and the Coronation, saw to it that our belfry gave forth a joyful sound; and at weddings he had been known to spare a little of his leisure to assist with the time-honoured practice of chiming the happy pair out of church. Now our Doctor was with the Army, but he sent an enthusiastic wire to his Deputy Captain bidding him; "Carry on!"

Sunday morning came, and as the ringers assembled – in jubilant spirits – from their several quarters of the Village, they heard ding-dong, ding-dong coming across the hill from our neighbouring village whose church has only two bells. We have five bells, but ding-dong was a very joyous and tuneful noise to be hearing on a November Sunday morning.

The ringers also heard another heart-rejoicing sound – the lowing of cattle. For by now we had cows again. It was a great day for the Village when Miss Moxam went to Gloucester and bought a cow. The entire population went down to Cleves to stare at Jersey Polly and at Molly, her calf.

By this time the ringers had reached the church gateway, passing the ancient yew tree and through the stone porch into the silent church. Soon they were within the curtained space where the bell pulls hang. Off came their coats – up went their hands. Hands used to handling plough and harrow, to making shells, and to the feel of a violin, grasped the ropes.

It was thought that after their long disuse those ropes would be stiff, and perhaps troublesome to handle – but, no, they were easy to pull. And, presently, out from the grey belfry floated triumphant voices, proclaiming over hill and valley the joy of the English people. This, as Mr. Churchill told us, "was our thanksgiving that in spite of all our errors and shortcomings we had been brought nearer to the frontiers of deliverance!"

The Allied Nations had stopped giving ground. They were now on the offensive, and the Village with an air of great relief and release from tension, ceased to allude to "the Muddle East", and spoke triumphantly of "our chaps out there".

Now the Fighting French were much in our minds. French North Africa was with us and against the common enemy. Hitler immediately over-ran all France and attempted to seize the French fleet at Toulon. To Marshal Pétain he sent a letter – fulsome, insincere and satanic – which could have deceived no one.

It is now past history that the French admirals scuttled their fleet, for indeed the eyes of the French people were opened. There was at last, in that tossed and anguished nation, a chance of unity and hope of a future – though as yet, and until the striking hour arrived, it must be with them as it was in 1870: "Think of it always, speak of it never."

So November passed away – that cheering, wonderful month, when the tide of our affairs turned, while our armies and their air support massed themselves in Tunisia. In some ways there was a lull after the exciting events of preceding weeks, but we were still at grips with an evil foe. Yet it was with bright flecks in the shadowed picture that we drew on towards the Austerity Christmas.

General Montgomery sent a Christmas greeting to the men of the Eighth Army, affirming that the Lord mighty in battles had given them the victory, and this message voiced the feeling which was uppermost in our hearts. Grateful and thankful we all were for the changes which had taken place between last Christmas and this.

Last Christmas Day Hong Kong had surrendered. Last Boxing Day Mr. Churchill was warning the United States, and the world, of a time of tribulation ahead. He was a true prophet, for we had experienced it – in North Africa, in Russia, in the Far East, close at home in our own City, and in our own Village.

It was a great thing for England that she could keep Christmas at all. And though our celebrations had to be simple – not to say austere – we did make it a celebration. Yet it was – to John and me – a queer Christmas without Bunty, who was spending it on duty in hospital. The children and their parents who, for so many years, have done their Christmassing with us, could not come either. Our guests this time were all strangers, but we were glad to have them. Some things had been taken, but here we were – still with our home, still with our lives.

Our church on Christmas morning was beautiful with evergreens and berries, and with trails of Old Man's Beard. Between the two windows was the memorial set up "in faith and love", and in memory of the village lads who fell in the last war. These were familiar names – old village names, known in and before the days of Oliver Cromwell.

Near the tablet was a bunch of roses. It is said that in Mr. Winch's garden one flower cannot be induced to bloom, and that is the last rose of summer. Even at Christmas he has roses, and there they were – dark red and pure white roses, filling the old church with their fragrance. They were speaking, so it seemed, of those short sweet lives laid down twenty-five years before.

I remembered Omar's words:

> Alas! that Spring should vanish with the Rose!
> That Youth's sweet-scented manuscript should close!

And once more there came to me the conviction that upon those sweet-scented manuscripts *finis* had not been written.

Christmas was followed by such mild and beautiful days that one could walk out and take the air. Going down-along through Church Mede, I came to that fold of the hill, where one can look down and see the Village, half hidden by its green setting of trees and meadowlands.

By the river was the old mill, the rushing weir, and the sheltered path to the woods.

I thought of the young men and women of Britain, and especially, of our very own men and women. Of Ann Frobisher, no longer galloping through Friary Wood on her chestnut Melody; Ann has joined the Wrens.

## THIS IS MY VILLAGE

Our Village dressmaker, Miss Derrick, has put down her needle to take up an electric drill. Edward's long waiting and training are over, and he is in Bomber Command. The young Olivia sews sails in a parachute factory. Ian Ellison is in the R.A.F.

Amaryllis serves in a Government canteen. Middle-aged men like Maxwell and Michael are "getting their papers". Mr. Bagshaw is nearly worried out of his life endeavouring to make every gallon of petrol do the work of two.

Self, our gas man, is too busy to put our lighter right, and Mate has gone long ago to the Middle East, while Mr. Flower, having lost most of his men, has become as elusive as a new kettle or a pound of onions.

And we others – who are not so important – still have our own tasks, and our own small contribution of courage to make.

We have learned to bear with the scarcity of crockery; we have found it possible to manage without eggs, and to share our homes with strangers.

Waiting in shops for our rations, wearing our old clothes, accepting the absence of our beloveds – we are determined to be, as Clemenceau said, "in it to the very end of the end."

Yes, from Church Mede, the Village with its water spouts, with its little houses tucked edgeways and sideways, looked very homelike and very beautiful. For our Village – which fought in the battle of Flanders, in Greece and Crete, at Singapore and at El Alamein; fought on the sea, under the sea, in the Battle of Britain, and with heroic Malta; our grumbling, friendly, warm-hearted, gossip-loving Village represents with ten thousand others of her kind, that free spirit – elemental, true and precious – which is, and will be, for ever England!

Solemnly, and with great earnestness, something which lies deep within me saluted her!